HYDROGEN COMPOUNDS

OF THE

GROUP IV ELEMENTS

F. G. A. STONE

Department of Chemistry
Harvard University

PRENTICE-HALL, INC.
Englewood Cliffs, N.J./1962

HYDROGEN COMPOUNDS

OF THE

GROUP IV ELEMENTS

HYDROGEN COMPOUNDS OF THE GROUP IV ELEMENTS

F. G. A. Stone

Library of Congress Catalog Card Number 62-14123

Printed in the United States of America

44825–C

PREFACE

In the last twenty years inorganic chemistry has grown rapidly in importance. This has come about through a variety of influences, one of the most important being the application of the techniques of physical chemistry to the solution of problems in inorganic chemistry. There are few chemists who have not been affected by the recent advances in inorganic chemistry. In their work organic chemists frequently use relatively new inorganic compounds such as the complex metal hydrides, of which perhaps lithium aluminum hydride is the best known, and many physical chemists, particularly those concerned with spectroscopy, have become interested in the properties of transition metal ions. It appears to be generally accepted, therefore, that the modern chemist, irrespective of his own area of specialization, will be at least somewhat familiar with the extraordinary development of such fields as the chemistry of the boron hydrides and their derivatives, the application of ligand field theory to the chemistry of the transition metals, and the new metallocene and metallarene compounds. Such subjects as these have received well-deserved publicity, but it is the opinion of the writer that certain other areas of inorganic chemistry, in which great advances have also occurred, deserve more attention from reviewers than they have received. Such an area of neglect is the chemistry of the hydrogen compounds of silicon, germanium, tin and lead.

Much information on these compounds has been gained during the last two decades through the efforts of chemists in many countries, and it can be argued that some of the new work in this field is as significant as the advances in other areas of inorganic chemistry. It is the purpose of this short volume to remedy this deficiency by reviewing the chemistry of the hydrogen compounds of the Group IV elements with emphasis on recent developments. The volume is not intended to be comprehensive in nature, but it will provide the reader with a survey of the work of scientists who have, among other things, predicted and demonstrated the coplanarity of the heavy atoms in the amine $(SiH_3)_3N$, devised methods for making hydrides such as SnH_4 or GeH_4 in such quantity that they need no longer be regarded as laboratory curiosities, and prepared such novel compounds as $KSiH_3$, SiH_3PI_2, $(GeH_3)_2S$ and $(CH_3)_3PbH$.

It is a pleasure to acknowledge the help and advice of Professor E. G. Rochow who in 1954 first interested me in the hydrides of silicon and its congeners. I am very grateful to Drs. T. D. Coyle, M. K. Wilson and R. A. Plowman who read and criticised the manuscript, and to Dr. E. A. V. Ebsworth who discussed with me some of his recent work. I am especially indebted to Miss E. Pitcher for her help in proof reading and other matters, and I wish to express my appreciation to my wife, Judith, for her help and understanding.

F. G. A. STONE

CONTENTS

TABLES

HYDROGEN COMPOUNDS

OF THE

GROUP IV ELEMENTS

ONE

GENERAL

CONSIDERATIONS

Following the early ideas of shared electron-pair bonds put forward by Langmuir[195] and Lewis,[198] the simplest binary hydrogen compounds of carbon, silicon, germanium, tin and lead would be expected to have the general formula, MH_4. As has long been known, in agreement with these early concepts of valency, all the Group IV elements form a hydride MH_4.

The hydrocarbons belong to the domain of organic chemistry and their properties will not be considered here, except insofar as they are related to those of hydrogen compounds of elements heavier than carbon in Group IV.

In order to account for the existence of numerous hydrocarbons on the one hand and of only a limited number of hydrides of silicon, germanium, tin and lead on the other, as well as to understand differences in behavior among these hydrides, it is necessary to apply concepts based on hybridization, relative electronegativity, and thermodynamic and kinetic considerations.

In the case of tin and lead the dearth of hydrides having metal—metal bonds must be attributed in some degree to the thermodynamic factor.

The strength of both tin—tin and lead—lead bonds is relatively low, probably somewhat less than 40 kcal. and 20 kcal., respectively.   This is to be compared with the carbon—carbon single bond strength of about 80 kcal. and a silicon—silicon bond strength in covalent silicon compounds of about 50 kcal.* In determining the relative stabilities of the hydrides also important to some extent must be the drop in M—H bond strengths in passing from carbon to lead, although some recent determinations and estimates of the Sn—H bond strength suggest that this factor may have been overrated.   For the hydrides MH_4 thermochemical bond energies decrease with increasing atomic number of M, *viz.* C—H, 99.3; Si—H, 76.5; Ge—H, 69.0; and Sn—H, 60.4 kcal.,[149] but the Sn—H bond is still a fairly strong linkage.   In spite of this, stannane decomposes at room temperature into tin and hydrogen.   The decomposition of this hydride, therefore, must occur through a route requiring but little activation energy.   No thermodynamic data is available for the hydride PbH_4 which, as will be described later, has but a fleeting existence.

Bond strength considerations in themselves, therefore, provide neither a satisfactory explanation for the limited number of silanes and germanes reported in the literature nor for the instability of Sn—H linkages, because the Si—H, Si—Si, Ge—H, Ge—Ge, and Sn—H bonds are all strong.   A more important reason for the existence of numerous hydrocarbons but of only a limited number of hydrides of silicon and the elements under silicon in Group IV lies in the fact that carbon is unique among the Group IV elements in possessing modes of bonding which are not available to elements below the first row of the periodic system.   In order to understand this restriction in the bonding modes of heavier elements, it is necessary to review briefly the concept of hybridization.

The four outer electrons of a Group IV atom in the monatomic gas state are described in terms of the notation $ns^2np_xnp_y(^3P_0)$.   Such an electronic configuration with two unpaired electrons implies divalency. In order to account for the known tendency of Group IV elements, and in

---

* As mentioned later the Si—Si bond energy in the hydride Si_2H_6 has been determined as 46.4 kcal.   It is necessary to remember that the strength of a bond between two atoms will depend in part on the nature of the groups linked to the atoms in question.   However, the conclusions drawn above concerning *relative* bond strengths may be regarded as true irrespective of this proviso.

particular carbon, to form four covalent bonds with four adjacent atoms, it became necessary to suggest promotion of one of the s electrons into the p_z orbital leading to a state $ns\ np_xnp_ynp_z$, spectroscopically described as ^5S. Although such a state is satisfactory in predicting tetravalency, it is not in accord with the observed geometry of those covalent compounds MR_4 (R = H, halogen, organo-groups, etc.) which have been investigated from a structural point of view. The ^5S state involves two different types of orbital, one of which, the s, is devoid of directional character. For this reason it is obvious that it cannot satisfactorily describe covalent compounds of the Group IV elements, the structures of many of which have long been known to involve four bonds from a central atom, inclined at equal angles of 109°28' to each other. Moreover, a large body of chemical and physical evidence indicates the complete equivalence of the four bonds in, for example, CH_4. In order to circumvent this difficulty further principles based on quantum mechanics were applied, and this suggested an abandonment of the clear-cut division between s and p orbitals, and led to the idea of mixed or hybridized orbitals. In the case of molecules MH_4 this mixing is termed sp^3 hybridization, and the calculations lead to four composite and equivalent atomic orbitals directed in four tetrahedral directions from the origin. The advantage of hybridized orbitals lies in their highly directional character, which results in a maximum overlapping of these orbitals with the appropriate orbitals of other atoms leading to the formation of stronger bonds. It is true that energy is required to induce hybridization, but this is more than compensated by the gain in energy through formation of stronger bonds. The bonding in the methane series of hydrocarbons can thus be interpreted in terms of employment by the carbon atoms of sp^3 hybrids to overlap suitable orbitals on adjacent atoms. The resultant tetrahedral arrangement is also shown by hydrides of the elements below carbon in Group IV like Si_2H_6, Ge_3H_8 and CH_3SnH_3, all of which are structurally similar to their carbon analogues, in line with a simple extension to higher quantum levels of the sp^3 hybrid concept. Now with carbon, tetrahedral hybrids are not the only hybrids which play a part in the chemistry of the element. It is also possible to mix s, p_x, and p_y orbitals to yield three sp^2 hybrids, or to mix the s and p_x orbitals to yield two sp hybrids. In the former situation the p_z orbital is left unchanged, while in the latter situation the p_y and p_z orbitals remain unaffected. The ethylenic state has for a number of years been conveniently described in terms of a so-called σ-bond involving overlap of two hybrid sp^2 orbitals, one from each carbon atom, along the axis joining the two carbon atoms, and a π-bond formed by the sideways overlap of the p_z orbitals of the two carbon atoms. For the acetylenic bond the unmixed p_y and p_z atomic orbitals are paired to form two π-bonds, while the two sp_x-hybrid orbitals overlap to form a σ-bond. The reader is referred elsewhere[57] for a refined treatment of the concept of hybridization, but the point to be noted here is that silicon and its congeners have an electronic configuration similar to carbon and are, therefore, potentially able to form hybrid orbitals of the sp^2 or sp variety. The elements below carbon in Group IV, however, do not form hydrides analogous to the olefins and acetylenes. A possible explanation for this fact is provided by a consideration of one of the most important criteria of covalent bond formation, namely, that bond strength depends on the amount of overlap of the two atomic orbitals paired together. Formation of two bonds of the σ, π-type as in ethylene, involving end-on overlap of sp^2 hybrids and sideways overlap of p_z orbitals, requires a relatively close approach of the two carbon nuclei. In silicon and the heavier Group IV elements the shorter internuclear distance required for good overlap in the σ and π-bonds of an ethylene-like (*e.g.* Si_2H_4) hydride would lead to strong repulsions between the nonbonding inner shell electrons of one atom and the valence electrons of its partner. Carbon has only two electrons under its $2s2p$ level whereas silicon has ten electrons under its $3s3p$ shell. This argument is an extension of a discussion by Pitzer[253] concerning inner shell-outer shell interactions, and although some reservations[230] have been expressed about Pitzer's[253] treatment on the grounds that inner shell repulsions, in spite of their importance, would be no larger for second-row than for first-row atoms, acceptance of the idea provides a satisfactory explanation as to why no hydrides of silicon, germanium or tin analogous to ethylene, acetylene, or the aromatic hydrocarbons have been reported [See footnote on page 6]. If this attractive idea is accepted, a corollary to it will be that the molecular hydrides of silicon and the heavier Group IV elements will be restricted to one series of compounds analogous to the paraffins. This restriction must result in a reduction in number of hydrides in passing from carbon to silicon. However, even if the idea is accepted that silicon and the Group IV elements will form only volatile hydrides analogous to the paraffin hydrocarbons, there still remains the possibility of a large number of compounds. In spite of this, as described in the next chapter, the highest member of the series Si_nH_{2n+2} claimed by Stock and his co-workers was assigned the formula Si_6H_{14}, it being recognized that the material was a mixture of isomers. Here the difficulty is one of lack of suitable synthetic methods for extending silicon-silicon or germanium-germanium atom chains, and this again stems from a limitation in the modes of bonding of the elements below carbon in Group IV. The great majority of methods available for ascending a homologous series of carbon atoms involves the use of reagents (e.g., CH_2N_2, $HCHO$, KCN) having unsaturated carbon atoms, or the use of reaction steps wherein carbon atoms are changed from an sp^3 to an sp^2 configuration. If the foregoing remarks about inner shell repulsions have any validity, it is clear that most preparative methods for building carbon chains cannot apply to silicon, germanium, or tin chemistry.

It is worthwhile following the concept of mixing atomic orbitals a little further because in recent years the hybridization idea has been used very extensively to interpret structural and chemical properties of molecular compounds, particularly hydrides and organometallics. With carbon, as with other first-row elements, hybridization is not limited to sp^3, sp^2 and sp states. Intermediate degrees of hybridization can occur. This is important in the chemistry and structure of the hydrides of elements of the Vth and VIth Groups, and in some of the compounds of the Group IV elements. In recent years, as additional and especially more accurate structural data have become available, the sharp division between atomic orbitals and hybrid atomic orbitals, e.g., between sp^3 and p, or sp^3 and sp^2, has had to be abandoned. Moreover, recently it has become clear that the description of ethylene in terms of a p_π—p_π bond and a σ-bond formed from sp^2-hybrid orbitals has been overstressed. An alternative description in terms of two "banana"-shaped bonds formed from four equivalent orbitals is equally correct and occasionally even superior.[71] The "banana" or bent bond description provides a better understanding as to why in ethylene two electrons with parallel spins tend to be on opposite sides of the plane of the molecule,[63] and the observation from infrared[1] and electron diffraction[23] studies that the H—C—H bond angle (*circa* 116°) is significantly less than 120°, the angle demanded by sp^2-hybridization. Bent bonds, it should be noted, with their overlap of essentially four sp^3 hybrids on either side of the axis joining the two atoms, imply for effective interaction a shorter internuclear distance than in a normal bond where the electron density is concentrated along the axis between the two atoms involved. Therefore, even if in the future theoretical chemists favor an abandonment of the distinction between σ- and π-electrons in carbon chemistry, for the reason mentioned previously, inner shell repulsions, silicon and other elements above the $2s^2 2p^6$ octet are unlikely to form hydrides in which the bonding can be described in terms of bent bonds based on s and p orbitals only.*

Another factor partly responsible for the scarcity of polysilanes, polygermanes and polystannanes is the reactivity of M—M and M—H

---

* Very recently the unique compound $(CH_3)_2Si:CHSi(CH_3)_3$ has been isolated from the pyrolysis products of tetramethylsilane.[120a] It is interesting to consider the possibility that in $(CH_3)_2Si:CHSi(CH_3)_3$ the silicon-carbon double bond does not comprise a silicon-carbon σ-bond and a silicon $(3p_\pi)$-carbon $(2p_\pi)$ π-bond, but that the π-component of the bond is formed by overlap of a $3pd_\pi$ hybrid of silicon and a $2p_\pi$ orbital of carbon. A pd_π hybrid of silicon might well be sufficiently elongated to overlap effectively with a p_π-orbital on an adjacent carbon atom. If this is the situation in $(CH_3)_2Si:CHSi(CH_3)_3$ the π-bond in this molecule would not be analogous to that in olefins but would be somewhat analogous to the π-bonds *believed* to occur in monomeric $(CH_3)_2SbBH_2$, and in platinum and other metal olefin complexes. Indeed, in several inorganic and semi-inorganic molecules π bonds formed from hybrids of p and d orbitals have been invoked.

Even more recently incorporation of a silicon atom into an aromatic system has been reported.[26a] Reduction of 1,1-dichlorosilacyclopentadiene with lithium aluminum hydride affords silacyclopentadiene $[(CH)_4SiH_2]$. The latter can be converted to the novel anion

with potassium sand in tetrahydrofuran. The absorption spectrum of the anion is very similar to that of the cyclopentadienide anion. The bonding in the silicon anion might well involve participation of the silicon d-orbitals, in a manner similar to that suggested above for $(CH_3)_2Si:CHSi(CH_3)_3$.

bonds compared with their carbon analogues. In the case of the silicon—hydrogen bond the direction of the bond polarity is such that the hydrogen is negative with respect to silicon. This is the reverse of the situation in C—H, N—H, or S—H bonds but is similar to that existing in the B—H, Be—H or Li—H bonds. The hydridic character of hydrogen in the silanes, as opposed to the protonic character of hydrogen in the hydrocarbons, makes the silanes susceptible to oxidation and to hydrolysis. In many respects the chemistry of the silanes resembles that of the boranes[298] more than that of the paraffin hydrocarbons. It is interesting to note that germanium—hydrogen and tin—hydrogen bonds are less polar in the sense $M^{\delta+}$—$H^{\delta-}$ than the silicon—hydrogen bond. This is especially true of the germanium—hydrogen bond, which is not quantitatively cleaved even with thirty per cent base.

Thermodynamic and kinetic factors also play a part in determining the reactivity of the silanes, germanes and stannanes. Thus in the case of silicon the molar heat of oxidation is more than twice that of carbon, and so if an oxygen source and the necessary activation energy are provided, Si—H, Si—C, Si—Si or certain other bonds from silicon are destroyed in favor of forming the Si—O linkage. This ever-present thermodynamic possibility is kinetically assisted by the ability of silicon to use its $3d$ orbitals to form favorable transition states or even definite complexes. In this respect silicon is strikingly different from carbon which like other first-row elements is limited to a covalency of four. The ability of silicon and its congeners to expand their valence shells opens the way to low energy reaction paths not possible with carbon. This will be discussed more fully later.

A hydride of a Group IV element may be defined as a molecule possessing a linkage M—H, where M = Si, Ge, Sn or Pb. If this definition is accepted, the simple binary compounds MH_4 may be regarded as the parent substances of a multitude of other hydrides since substitution of up to three of the hydrogen atoms still leaves a molecule having an M—H bond. Common substituents are alkyl or aryl groups, and to a lesser extent amino-, alkoxy-, or thiogroups. If the substituents are organic groups, the resulting compounds can also be treated as organometal or metalloidal compounds [e.g., $(C_2H_5)_3SnH$ or $(CH_3)_3SiH$], while if the substituents are halogens, the derivatives produced (e.g., $SiHCl_3$) can be regarded as halides.   The relationship between Group IV element hydrides on the one hand and the halides and organometallic compounds on the other is illustrated by the existence of molecules containing linkages to carbon, halogen and hydrogen, e.g., CH_3SiH_2Cl.

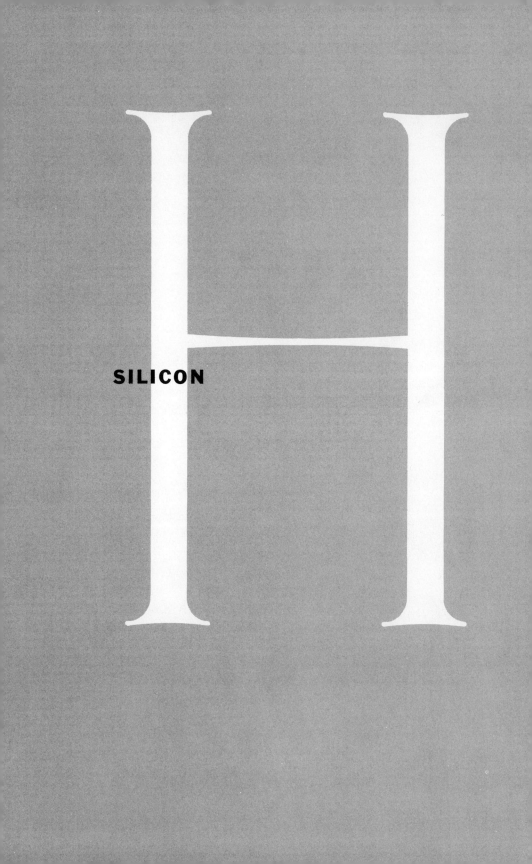

SILICON

THE SILICON HYDRIDES

AND RELATED COMPOUNDS

For over fifty years before Stock began his classic work on the boranes and the silanes, the hydrides of silicon were observed intermittently. Thus in 1857 Wöhler and Buff[344] reported that when aluminum silicide was dissolved in hydrochloric acid, volatile air-sensitive materials were produced. It was not possible, however, to fully characterize the silanes until Stock and his co-workers developed vacuum techniques for the manipulation of air-sensitive compounds. The early work by Stock on the simple silanes, Si_nH_{2n+2}, has been summarized by him in his Baker lectures.[293]

A. *Preparation of the Silanes*

Stock and his co-workers prepared the silanes from the reaction between hydrochloric acid and magnesium silicide. Only about one-fourth of the silicon content of the magnesium silicide was converted to silicon hydrides, this being approximately distributed as 40% SiH_4, 30% Si_2H_6, 15% Si_3H_8, 10% Si_4H_{10}, and 5% higher hydrides. Hydrogen was another reaction product.   Following the work of Stock the next most significant advance in this field came on the discovery that silane and disilane could be obtained in 70-80% yield from the reaction between magnesium silicide and ammonium bromide in liquid ammonia.[169, 170]   This reaction, using ammonium chloride instead of ammonium bromide, has received further attention quite recently.[53]   In the original procedure[169, 170] use of specially prepared magnesium silicide gave a mixture containing up to 60% of disilane.   The more efficient conversion of silicon in a silicide to silanes by this procedure, as opposed to Stock's method, is no doubt due to the inertness of the silicon—hydrogen bond to ammonia.

With the advent of chromatography it was to be anticipated that this technique would be applied to the separation and identification of hydride mixtures.   It is, therefore, interesting that the mixture of silanes obtained by treating magnesium silicide with phosphoric acid has been separated by vapor phase chromatography into 21 components.[35]   By a study of their nuclear magnetic resonance spectra, the hydrides n-Si_4H_{10}, n-Si_5H_{12}, and iso-Si_5H_{12} were identified.   Another compound of formula Si_4H_{10} was obtained, and the silanes n-Si_6H_{14}, n-Si_7H_{16}, and n-Si_8H_{18} were also tentatively identified.

It was not until the reducing properties of lithium aluminum hydride were described[110] that silanes of many types became accessible in relatively large quantity.[111]   Indeed, the discovery of lithium aluminum hydride and related complex hydrides has revolutionized not only the preparation of the silanes but also that of many other covalent hydrides.[296]   Addition of a silicon halide to lithium aluminum hydride in ether solution results in the formation in high yield of a silane.   Silicon tetrachloride and lithium aluminum hydride afford silane,[110, 247] but the method may be extended to Si_2Cl_6 and Si_3Cl_8, which yield Si_2H_6 and Si_3H_8 respectively.   Organosilicon halides are reduced to organosilanes by lithium aluminum hydride, a reaction used extensively for synthetic purposes, e.g.,

$$(n\text{-}C_3H_7)_2SiCl_2 + LiAlH_4 \xrightarrow{(C_2H_5)_2O} (n\text{-}C_3H_7)_2SiH_2 \qquad (111)$$
$$\text{80\% yield}$$

$$(C_6H_5)_2SiCl_2 + LiAlH_4 \xrightarrow{(C_2H_5)_2O} (C_6H_5)_2SiH_2 \qquad (27)$$
$$\text{76\%}$$

$$CH_2:CHSiCl_3 + LiAlH_4 \xrightarrow[\text{reflux}]{\text{dioxane}} CH_2:CHSiH_3 \qquad (312)$$
$$80\text{-}90\%$$

$$Cl_2HSiCH_2SiCl_3 + LiAlH_4 \xrightarrow{(C_2H_5)_2O} H_3SiCH_2SiH_3 \qquad (101)$$
$$52\%$$

$$CHCl_2SiCl_3 + LiAlH_4 \xrightarrow{(n\text{-}C_4H_9)_2O} CHCl_2SiH_3 \qquad (173)$$
$$86\%$$

$$(CH_2SiCl_2)_3{}^* + LiAlH_4 \xrightarrow{(C_2H_5)_2O} (CH_2SiH_2)_3 \qquad (127)$$

It has also been found possible to reduce certain silicon halides with alkali metal hydrides. Thus lithium hydride suspended in refluxing dioxane, when treated with diethyldichlorosilane, afforded diethylsilane in 66% yield,[111] and chloromethylsilane has been obtained by refluxing chloromethyltrichlorosilane with lithium hydride in di*iso*pentyl ether.[255] In the latter reaction, however, the yield of the desired compound CH_2ClSiH_3 is poor, and it is best prepared (78% yield) by treating $CH_2ClSiCl_3$ with lithium aluminum hydride at 0° in dibutyl ether.[173] The compound $CH_2(SiH_3)_2$ has been obtained from $CH_2(SiCl_3)_2$ and lithium hydride.[25]

The silicon halides are not the only silicon compounds which yield silanes with lithium aluminum hydride. The silicon—oxygen bond in many compounds is reduced by the double hydride. Thus tri-*n*-propyl-silane and several other organosilanes have been prepared by heating the appropriate organoalkoxysilanes with lithium aluminum hydride.[334] Alternatively, alkoxysilanes may first be treated with aluminum chloride and the mixture subsequently reduced to silanes with lithium aluminum hydride. In this reaction, however, the alkoxysilanes are presumably first converted to halosilanes.[334] Further examples of cleavage of silicon—

---

* This novel crystalline heterocyclic compound is one of several products that can be obtained from the reaction between methylene dichloride and silicon in the presence of copper. It is also formed by pyrolysis of methyltrichloro- or dimethyl-dichlorosilane. Much important work has recently been done in the area of pyrolysis of organosilicon compounds. Understandably many products are obtained as complex mixtures, but by careful experimentation, including extensive use of vapor phase chromatography, it has been possible to characterize several unusual heterocyclic silicon compounds having six membered rings of alternate silicon and carbon atoms. See references 118, 120, 122, 126, 127, and 128.

oxygen bonds by lithium aluminum hydride are provided by the formation of silane from the reactions between the double hydride and hexachlorodisiloxane $[(Cl_3Si)_2O]$,[117, 273]* trialkoxydisiloxanes, e.g., $[(C_3H_7O)_3Si]_2O$,[117] or orthosilicates, e.g., $Si(OC_2H_5)_4$.[117] These reactions occur even at room temperature, and it was further observed[117] that the Si—O—Si groups of silicones were cleaved with lithium aluminum hydride, and that even quartz sand and the double hydride slowly developed silane. Furthermore, even when hexachlorodisiloxane is treated with the mild reducing agent, sodium borohydride, only silane is formed. The halogen atoms of $(Cl_3Si)_2O$ are not selectively reduced to yield disiloxane, $(SiH_3)_2O$.[273]

The advent of lithium aluminum hydride as a reagent for synthetic work has not prevented investigators from continuing to describe other reactions leading to the formation of silanes. At present, however, these other routes to the hydrides appear to be only of academic interest. Examples of such reactions are the formation of silane from magnesium silicide and hydrazine hydrochloride in hydrazine,[106] a combination of reagents related to the magnesium silicide-ammonium halide-ammonia system,[169, 170] and formation of silane when magnesium silicide is heated with ammonium bromide, trimethylammonium hydrochloride, or ethylenediamine hydrochloride.[160]

As a conclusion to this section describing the preparation of the silanes, it is important to take note of one reaction of great practical importance leading to formation of silicon—hydrogen bonds, and which does not involve lithium aluminum hydride, and uses only readily available materials. Over a century ago the compounds $SiHCl_3$ and $SiHI_3$ were prepared by heating silicon in a current of the appropriate dry hydrogen halide.[45] Later workers obtained trichlorosilane by the action of hydrogen chloride at elevated temperatures on magnesium silicide,[131] ferrosilicon,[329] vanadium silicide,[228] and copper silicide.[293] Following

---

* During reduction of the halide Si_2Cl_6 with lithium aluminum hydride to give disilane, monosilane has also been observed as a product. Formation of the monosilane has frequently been attributed to cleavage of the Si—Si bond in hexachlorodisilane with lithium aluminum hydride. It is more probable, however, that the monosilane is derived from hexachlorodisiloxane a frequent impurity in hexachlorodisilane.

the preparation of SiHBr$_3$ from gaseous hydrogen bromide and silicon,[274] the preparation of trichlorosilane from hydrogen chloride and silicon was greatly improved.[33] If hydrogen is mixed with hydrogen halide in reactions of this type, dihalosilanes as well as trihalosilanes are formed, and both SiHCl$_3$ and SiH$_2$Cl$_2$ are made on an industrial scale in this manner. Alternatively, trichlorosilane itself may be disproportionated to dichlorosilane (15% yield) by heating to 300-400° in the presence of acid catalysts of the metallic halide type, e.g., AlCl$_3$, FeCl$_3$, BF$_3$, etc.[102] The ready accessibility of tri- and di-chlorosilane has led to their wide use as intermediates, as described in a later section. However, both these chlorosilanes (silyl chlorides) were first thoroughly characterized by Stock[293] who, as described in the next section, obtained SiH$_2$Cl$_2$ from SiH$_4$.

B. Properties of the Silanes

In the course of their researches, Stock and his collaborators isolated and determined many physical properties of the silanes SiH$_4$, Si$_2$H$_6$, Si$_3$H$_8$, and Si$_4$H$_{10}$ (Table 1), claiming in addition, Si$_5$H$_{12}$ and Si$_6$H$_{14}$ as mixtures of isomers. As mentioned above, the mixture of gases produced by treating magnesium silicide with acid has now been subjected to a vapor phase chromatographic analysis showing the presence of two hydrides Si$_4$H$_{10}$, as well as n- and iso-Si$_5$H$_{12}$. It is possible that the properties of Si$_4$H$_{10}$ obtained by Stock, and given in Table 1, refer to a mixture of isomers.

TABLE 1. THE SILANES.[293]

Compound	M.P.	B.P.*	Compound	M.P.	B.P.*
SiH$_4$	−185°	−111.9°	Si$_3$H$_8$	−117.4°	52.9°
Si$_2$H$_6$	−132.5°	−14.5°	Si$_4$H$_{10}$	−84.3°	107.4°

* B.P.'s expressed in this and succeeding tables in this book were obtained by extrapolation of vapor pressure equations, unless a B.P. at a certain pressure is given.

Whereas both SiH$_4$ and Si$_2$H$_6$ are gases at ordinary temperatures, the higher silanes are liquids.

The thermal stability of the silanes is much less than that of the analogous paraffin hydrocarbons, and decreases with increasing molecular weight.   Above about 500° all the hydrides decompose to silicon and hydrogen.   However, limited exposure of a silane to less than red heat yields a mixture of other volatile hydrides of lower molecular weight, as well as solid silicon-hydrogen containing materials and hydrogen, e.g.,

$$Si_5H_{12} \longrightarrow 2(SiH)_x + Si_2H_6 + SiH_4$$

Such reactions are reminiscent of the cracking of hydrocarbons, but differ in that they occur at a lower temperature.   Thus, disilane begins perceptible decomposition near 300°, yielding hydrogen, silane, silicon, and small amounts of higher hydrides.   If the pyrolysis of Si_2H_6 or Si_3H_8 is carried out in the presence of hydrogen, the proportion of monosilane produced is raised.   This led to the suggestion that the decomposition reactions involve silyl $(SiH_3 \cdot)$ radicals,[95] but as mentioned on page 50 other decomposition mechanisms would explain this result.   If the silane pyrolysis is conducted in the presence of ethylene, the hydrocarbon is polymerized to some extent with some incorporation of silicon in the polymer.[95]   Subsequently, as described below, other workers have studied the reaction between the Si—H bond and olefins and have noted important addition reactions.   An electric discharge or ultraviolet irradiation also brings about some decomposition of a silane.[99]

The solid non-volatile silicon hydrides formed in some of these decomposition reactions are undoubtedly polymeric.   In this respect they resemble the non-volatile hydrides of boron, germanium, tin, phosphorus and certain other elements.   The polysilanes $(SiH_n)_x$ are light brown solids with a variable hydrogen content.   As hydrogen is lost on heating, they darken in color.   Because of their somewhat intractable nature, they have been but little studied.   They have also been formed by reactions other than the thermal decomposition of silane.   Treatment of $SiHBr_3$ with magnesium in ether solution affords a yellow solid polymer $(SiH)_n$, slowly oxidized in dry air but rapidly in moist air.[271]   The material withstands neutral water reasonably well, but alkaline solution brings about a violent reaction with release of hydrogen.

Very pure silane can be mixed with air under certain conditions of temperature and pressure without explosion,[98] but under other conditions, especially when silane contains traces of higher silanes or impurities, the hydride inflames violently.   Disilane and the higher hydrides are all spontaneously inflammable and explosive in air, even well below room temperature. The three hydrides, SiH_4, Si_2H_6, and Si_3H_8, form a graded series in which inflammability increases with molecular weight.[98]

The powerful reducing properties of the silanes were immediately recognized by Stock and his co-workers,[293] who noted that potassium permanganate is reduced to manganese(IV) oxide, iron(III) salts are reduced to iron(II), and copper(II) salts are reduced to a material claimed to be copper hydride. It has been claimed that use can be made for analytical purposes of the ability of Si—H bonds to reduce metal halides. The reaction

$$SiH_4 + 8HgCl_2 + 4H_2O \longrightarrow Si(OH)_4 + 4Hg_2Cl_2 + 8HCl$$

proceeds with a complete consumption of silane.[116] Since the amount of mercury(I) chloride produced in a reaction of this type can be found iodometrically, the Si—H content of the silicon compound taken for reaction can be determined. The method has been applied to $(C_2H_5)_2SiH_2$ and $SiHCl_3$, as well as SiH_4, in order to establish its generality.

The silanes have a great affinity for halogens. After Stock and his co-workers[293] discovered that silane reacted explosively with chlorine or bromine at ambient temperatures, they found it convenient to introduce halogen into the silane structure by treating the silane with hydrogen halide in the presence of an aluminum halide, using only mild heating. Without the aluminum halide as catalyst, the halogen substitution reaction does not take place even at elevated temperatures. Stock and his collaborators employed only hydrogen chloride and hydrogen bromide in their studies, but later workers[91] extended these reactions to hydrogen iodide, thereby obtaining SiH_3I and SiH_2I_2, and making the reactions,

$$SiH_4 + HX \xrightarrow{AlX_3} SiH_3X + H_2$$

$$SiH_3X + HX \xrightarrow{AlX_3} SiH_2X_2 + H_2$$

quite general for X = Cl, Br or I. It should be noted, however, that it has recently been found possible to prepare iodosilanes in substantial quantities without recourse to silane, a hazardous reagent. The new method involves cleavage of the Si—C bond of a phenylsilane with hydrogen iodide at room temperature. In this manner chlorophenylsilane[14] or phenylsilane[123] afford silyl iodide, and diphenylsilane[14] affords silyl

diiodide.   It had earlier been observed that phenylsilane and hydrogen
bromide react to give silyl bromide.[219]   This has been confirmed by
Fritz and Kummer,[125a,b] who have established the generality of the
reaction,

$$C_6H_5SiH_3 + HX \longrightarrow C_6H_6 + SiH_3X$$
$$(X = F, Cl, Br \text{ or } I)$$

and shown that this type of cleavage process can be used to prepare
silicon halides of the type SiH_2XY^*:

$$C_6H_5SiH_2X + HY \longrightarrow C_6H_6 + SiH_2XY$$
$$(X, Y = Cl, Br, \text{ or } I)$$

Recently Stock's experimental procedure for making silyl bromide
has been modified to yield relatively large quantities of product.   When
streams of gaseous silane and hydrogen bromide are passed over aluminum
bromide supported on asbestos at 80-100°, SiH_3Br and SiH_2Br_2 are formed
and can be separated by distillation through a 11-plate column.[238]

As mentioned in the previous section, dichlorosilane is obtained
commercially directly from silicon or ferrosilicon.   Stock[293] found that
SiH_2Cl_2 reacted with SiH_4 in the presence of aluminum chloride to yield
SiH_3Cl, so if dichlorosilane is available it is a convenient starting point
for the preparation of silyl chloride.

Later workers have had more success than Stock in controlling the
reaction between silane and a halogen.   Thus silyl bromide has been
made in about 90% yield by treating solid bromine at −40° to −50°
with silane vapor.[306]

The report[146] that passage of the vapors of silicon tetrachloride and
formaldehyde over alumina at 350-500° yields SiH_3Cl and SiH_2Cl_2 has
been shown to be incorrect.[129]   The principal products are hydrogen
chloride, methyl chloride, chlorosiloxanes or silica, plus small amounts
of methylene chloride.

A further method for introducing halogen atoms into a silane structure, but which does not work with monosilane, is *via* the reaction,

$$Si_3H_8 + 4CHCl_3 \xrightarrow{AlCl_3} Si_3H_4Cl_4 + 4CH_2Cl_2$$

Although this reaction, and that between Si_2H_6 or Si_3H_8 and hydrogen
chloride with aluminum halide catalyst, enabled Stock and his co-

---

* Compounds of this kind (H_2SiClI, $H_2SiClBr$, and H_2SiBrI) disproportionate
easily into SiH_2X_2 and SiH_2Y_2.

workers[293] to obtain chlorides of the higher silanes, pure compounds were not isolated, only mixtures of isomers being obtained.

The hydrides of silicon do not release hydrogen when treated with pure water in quartz vessels, but their Si—H bonds are so easily broken down in alkaline solution that if ordinary glass is added, its alkali content is sufficient to bring about hydrolysis of the silane.*[293] Strongly acidified water also causes hydrolysis of silicon hydrides. With excess of alcohols, in the presence of the corresponding alkoxide ions as catalysts, silane forms tetraalkoxysilanes and hydrogen.[247]

$$SiH_4 + 4ROH \xrightarrow{OR^-} Si(OR)_4 + 4H_2$$

The claim[247] that methanol does not react with silane has been shown[290, 290a] to be incorrect. At room temperature monosilane and methanol produce di-, tri- and tetramethoxysilanes, and hydrogen, provided a liquid phase is present. The rate of reaction is increased by the presence of copper metal. As discussed later, copper exerts a similar catalytic effect on the alcoholysis of organosilanes. Gaseous methanol and gaseous silane do not react at room temperature in the absence of other reagents, but copper metal acts as a catalyst leading to the formation of a mixture of methoxysilanes and hydrogen. Methoxysilane (silyl methyl ether) was not isolated from these reactions but was obtained by methanolysis of the solid adduct $(CH_3)_3N, SiH_3I$, as described below.

It has recently been found possible to characterize the compound potassium silyl, $KSiH_3$.[258] This is of particular significance in view of the fact that the compounds $NaGeH_3$ and $NaSnH_3$, as described later in this volume, are also known. A solution of $KSiH_3$ in monoglyme† can be prepared from silane and potassium or sodium-potassium alloy, or from disilane and potassium hydride. Filtration, followed by slow evaporation of the solvent affords $KSiH_3$, as moisture- and air-sensitive colorless crystals having the sodium chloride crystal structure. Potassium silyl reacts with hydrogen chloride to give silane and potassium chloride, with methyl chloride to give methylsilane, and with water to give hydrogen.

---

* Basic hydrolysis is quantitative, one molecule of hydrogen being released for each Si—H and Si—Si bond present. The hydrolysis reaction, therefore, provides a useful analytical tool.

† 1,2-Dimethoxyethane.

All these reactions are quantitative, as is the thermal decomposition of $KSiH_3$ at 240° in vacuo to yield hydrogen. Potassium silyl also reacts with silyl bromide, with silicon tetrabromide and with diborane but the nature of the products is complex. Thus with the expectation of preparing 1,1,1-trideuterodisilane, trideuterobromosilane was added to potassium silyl in monoglyme. A white solid formed, probably potassium bromide, along with a mixture of deuterosilanes, deuterodisilanes, and partially protonated deuterobromosilane. Bridge-bonded transition states (sp^3d hybridized Si) I and II have been proposed to account for the products:

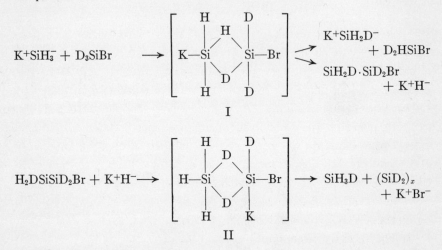

Although it is reported that silane does not react with the Grignard reagent or diethylzinc, it does react fairly readily with phenylsodium or organolithium compounds.[247] The nature of the solvent in these reactions plays an important part in determining the nature of the final product. For example, ethyllithium and silane afford tetraethylsilane (63% yield) when the reaction is carried out in diethyl ether, whereas with petroleum ether as solvent the two reagents yield triethylsilane (36% yield) and diethylsilane (27% yield). Phenyllithium and silane in diethyl ether afford tetraphenylsilane in 40% yield. The ability of organolithium compounds to remove hydride ion from a silicon hydride is quite general, and may be represented by the equation,

$$R_xSiH_{4-x} + (4 - x)R'Li \longrightarrow R_xSiR'_{4-x} + (4 - x)LiH$$

R and R' may be an alkyl or aryl group, and x may have the values zero,[247] one,[232] two[247] or three.[28,136,226]

Silane reacts with olefins to form organosilanes. With ethylene, in a static system at 450°, the hydride yields ethyl-, diethyl- and triethyl-silane, as well as a mixture of methylsilanes and compounds of higher molecular weight.[113] Recently the reactions between olefins and silane have been carried out in a stepwise fashion yielding below 250° $RSiH_3$, and then from 250° to 450° producing mostly R_2SiH_2 with small amounts of R_3SiH and R_4Si.[345] Because the initially formed products underwent extensive decomposition under the conditions used in the original work,[113] the thermal reaction between silane and ethylene was studied at normal pressures in a flow system.[335] Under these conditions the reaction products are $C_2H_5SiH_3$, $(C_2H_5)_2SiH_2$, Si_2H_6, Si_3H_8, and a compound believed to be $C_2H_5Si_2H_5$. When a mixture of silane and acetylene is circulated through a heated tube, ethynyldivinylsilane, $(CH_2:CH)_2SiH(C:CH)$, is the principal product. On the other hand, when a mixture of silane and acetylene is activated photochemically, vinylsilane is the major reaction product. The ability of the silicon—hydrogen bond to add to carbon—carbon double or triple bonds was known[21,49,133,284] before these direct reactions between silane and ethylene, or silane and acetylene were reported. The earlier work was concerned principally with halosilanes like $SiHCl_3$, but more recently much work has been done on the addition of organosilanes to carbon—carbon double bonds.[78]

In concluding this section, one other reaction of monosilane is of interest. If a mixture of silane and boron trichloride is irradiated with ultraviolet light and a source of methyl radicals is present (azomethane), diborane is formed in 67% yield.[265]

C. Derivatives of Silane — Their Preparation and Chemical Reactions

1. HALOSILANES

The preparation of halosilanes of the type $SiH_{4-n}X_n$ ($n = 1,2,3$), with the exception of the fluorides, has been described in previous sections of this chapter. The fluorosilanes can readily be prepared by fluorination of chlorosilanes using metal fluorides. Thus treatment of trichloro-,[34,90] dichloro-,[90] or monochlorosilane[90] with antimony trifluoride yields trifluoro-, difluoro-, and monofluorosilane, respectively.

Stock and his co-workers were the first to report the disilanyl halides, Si_2H_5Cl and Si_2H_5Br, but neither compound was obtained pure, in part due to occurrence of ready disproportionations,

$$2SiH_3SiH_2X \longrightarrow Si_2H_4X_2 + Si_2H_6$$

Disilanyl iodide is much more stable, and has been obtained in good yields via the reaction,

$$Si_2H_6 + HI \xrightarrow{AlI_3} Si_2H_5I + H_2$$

which occurs at room temperature.[327] The compound is spontaneously inflammable in air, and reacts with silver bromide to afford Si_2H_5Br.[328a]

All the monohalosilanes tend to disproportionate into silane and the dihalosilanes, with the tendency for disproportionation decreasing along the series SiH_3F, SiH_3Cl, SiH_3Br, SiH_3I. In the latter compound the effect is negligible. These disproportionation reactions are reversible to some extent, since, as mentioned previously, dichlorosilane and silane react in the presence of aluminum chloride to give monochlorosilane. These halogen transfer reactions have similar counterparts in boron chemistry[41] and probably proceed via a four-center transition state,[212] the occurrence of which is made easy by virtue of the ability of silicon to assume a coordination number greater than four.

Of the SiH_3X compounds, only the bromide is spontaneously inflammable in air, although the other monohalosilanes are readily oxidized and will burn if ignited. There is a gradual decrease in inflammability as monosilane is progressively halogenated.[100]

All the halosilanes are hydrolyzed rapidly by water. The monohalosilanes yield disiloxane $(SiH_3)_2O$, discussed further below, and the hydrogen halide. The di- and tri-halosilanes, however, afford polymeric materials and the appropriate HX compound. For example, with water trichlorosilane probably produces $HSi(OH)_3$ as an intermediate, which condenses to give a polymeric solid of empirical composition, $HSiO_{1.5}$. This material, which has a mica-like structure,[338] is probably related to siloxene (Si_2H_2O), a white solid spontaneously inflammable in air, and

TABLE 2. THE HALOSILANES AND SOME RELATED COMPOUNDS.

Compound	M.P.	B.P.	Reference	Compound	M.P.	B.P.	Reference
SiH_3F	...	-98.6°	90	$SiHF_3$	-131°	-95°	90
SiH_3Cl	-118.1°	-30.4°	293	$SiHCl_3$	-127°	31.8°	293
SiH_3Br	-94°	1.9°	293	$SiHBr_3$	73.5°	111.8°	272
SiH_3I	-57.0°	45.4°	91	$SiHI_3$	8°	220°	261
				$SiHClF_2$	~ -144°	~ -50°	34
				$SiHCl_2F$	-149.5°	-18.4°	34
SiH_2F_2	-122°	-77.8°	90				
SiH_2Cl_2	-122°	8.3°	293				
SiH_2Br_2	-70.1°	66°	293	SiH_3CN	32.4°	49.6°	213
SiH_2I_2	-1.0°	149.5°	91	SiH_3NCS	-51.8°	84.0°	213
Si_2H_5Br	...	69.5°	328a	Si_2H_5I	-86.1°	102.8°	327

obtained from the reaction between calcium silicide and an alcohol-hydrochloric acid mixture.   Siloxene may well have a structure similar to $HSiO_{1.5}$ but with Si—Si bonds as well as Si—H and Si—O linkages.[175,176]

Treatment of a halosilane with aqueous base leads to rupture of Si—H bonds as well as breakage of the Si—X bonds so that complete decomposition takes place. This is in contrast to the reaction between chlorosilanes and ethanol in benzene, or better $(CH_3)_2NC_6H_5$, which yields ethoxysilanes, e.g., a mixture of $C_2H_5OSiHCl_2$, $(C_2H_5O)_2SiHCl$, and $(C_2H_5O)_3SiH$ from $HSiCl_3$ and C_2H_5OH.[194]

The hydrolysis, alcoholysis, aminolysis, and certain other substitution reactions involving silicon compounds probably proceed through a mechanism of the S_N2 type, common in carbon chemistry.[78]   A mechanism of this type will involve a pentacoordinate transition state irrespective of whether substitution is occurring at a silicon atom or at a carbon atom.   In view of this similarity one may well inquire why hydrolysis of silyl halides is very fast while the hydrolysis of alkyl halides is slow.   A reasonable explanation why certain substitution reactions occur with silicon compounds whereas they do not occur, or else take place more slowly, with carbon compounds can be derived from a consideration of the energies of the transition states in the two cases.   During displacement of one group by another the highest energy state will be trigonal bipyramidal in shape, and in the case of silicon, therefore, both entering and leaving groups can be regarded as being held by silicon sp^3d hybrid orbitals.   This transition state would surely require less energy to reach, and thereby give rise to faster reactions, than the situation with carbon where entering and leaving groups are postulated to share a p orbital, the $3d$ orbitals of carbon being much less accessible than those of silicon.   Thus the availability of d orbitals on silicon facilitates the attack of a nucleophilic reagent irrespective of whether or not a detectable pentacoordinate silicon complex is produced.*   In principle intermediates such as $HO^- \rightarrow SiH_4$, $H_2O \rightarrow SiH_3I$, or $H_3N \rightarrow SiH_2Cl_2$ may yet be revealed by suitable experimentation.   In forming a pentacoordinate state, or with certain combinations of reagents possibly forming a definite complex, tetracoordinate silicon can be regarded as displaying Lewis acidity and the attacking

---

* For an important discussion of the mechanism of substitution at a silicon atom the reader is recommended to consult reference 78.

reagent Lewis base character. Unlike trivalent compounds of the Group III elements, with potentially vacant p-orbitals, tetravalent silicon compounds are very weak acids. Thus the complex $(CH_3)_3N \cdot BH_3$ is known whereas $(CH_3)_3N \cdot SiH_4$ is not. The formation of the pentacoordinate intermediate will, therefore, depend on the base strength of the attacking reagent and on how the acceptor power of silicon can be increased by changing the nature of substituent groups. Thus silane does not react with pure water or ammonia,* both very weak bases, but does react rapidly with the much stronger electron-pair donor hydroxide ion. On the other hand, silyl halides react easily with water and amines, presumably because the presence of an electron withdrawing halogen atom on silicon increases its Lewis acidity to a point where formation of a pentacoordinate intermediate such as $CH_3(H_2)N \rightarrow SiH_3Br$ is possible. The fact that silyl halides react with water, ammonia, amines, or alcohols with fission of Si—X bonds in preference to Si—H bonds can be understood because of the greater polarity of Si—X linkages. Thus the process $\geqslant SiH \rightarrow \geqslant Si^+ + H^-$ requires 250 kcal. mole^{-1} whereas the process $\geqslant SiBr \rightarrow \geqslant Si^+ + Br^-$ requires only 179 kcal. mole^{-1}.[78] Moreover, the greater tendency for silyl chlorides, bromides or iodides compared with silyl fluorides to react with nucleophilic reagents can be explained in part in terms of the greater degree of dative π-bonding in Si—X bonds when X is F, an effect which will render the silicon d- orbitals less available for use in forming a low energy transition state with five bonds from silicon of the sp^3d type.† The greater strength of fluorine—silicon bonds compared with those between silicon and other halogen atoms may also be important.[78]

By treating a silyl halide with a base having no protonic hydrogen bonded to the donor atom, so that elimination of a small molecule does not occur, it is sometimes possible to isolate an adduct, e.g., $(CH_3)_3N$, SiH_3I. A useful summary and discussion of these substances, as well as

---

* There is a rapid reaction between silane and ammonia in the presence of amide ion: $SiH_4 + 4NH_3 \longrightarrow 4H_2 + [Si(NH_2)_4]_x$.

† The reader is reminded that even though fluorine is more electronegative than chlorine, boron trichloride is a stronger Lewis acid than boron trifluoride. See reference 297 for a discussion of the many factors which determine the electron acceptor powers of main group elements.

the related compounds formed by silicon halides, e.g., $(CH_3)_3N$, SiF_4, has recently been given by Aylett.[13]   There has been no general agreement on the structure of the various adducts which include such substances as:

$$(CH_3)_3P, SiH_3I \qquad C_5H_5N, SiBr_4 \qquad (CH_3)_3N, SiH_2Cl_2$$

$$[(CH_3)_3N]_2, SiH_3I \qquad (CH_3)_3N, SiCl_4 \qquad (CH_3)_3N, SiHF_3$$

On the basis of conductivity data some of these compounds, e.g., $(CH_3)_3N$, SiH_3X, have been formulated as quaternary compounds.   However, the fact that a silicon compound containing an Si—X bond (X = halogen) dissolves in an ionizing solvent such as acetonitrile to give a conducting solution does not necessarily mean that the silicon compound is ionic in nature.   It is difficult to remove the last traces of water from the solvent with the result that on addition of the silicon compound hydrolysis may occur with formation of the strong electrolyte HX, which although generated in only trace amounts can give rise to a finite conductivity.[314]   A compound such as $[(CH_3)_3N]_2SiH_3I$ or $[(CH_3)_2SO]_2SiF_4$ can reasonably be formulated with a hexacoordinate silicon atom, with sp^3d^2 hybridization, like the silicon atom in the SiF_6^{-2} ion.   It is tempting at first sight to suggest that most of the adducts of composition "Ligand, $SiH_{4-n}X_n$ (n = 1 to 4)" are complexes of pentacoordinate silicon but it seems more probable that they involve an octahedral arrangement of ligands around silicon, made possible by the presence of silicon-halogen-silicon bridges so that the structures are polymeric in nature.[108]   The thermal stability of many of the adducts is low and several have been shown to be completely dissociated in the gas phase at room temperature while others, for example $(CH_2)_4O$, SiH_3I exist only well below $0°$.   Their study, therefore, is not easy.

Silyl halides, SiH_3X, do not react with magnesium in a manner analogous to the alkyl halides.   Treatment of silyl iodide with magnesium in di*iso*amyl ether affords hydrogen, silane and silicon.[91]   Silyl bromide on the other hand reacts only slightly with magnesium to give small amounts of silane and hydrogen.[318]   Moreover, while SiH_3Cl is inert to a Würtz-type reaction, SiH_3I does react with sodium to give disilane.[91]

The main importance of the halosilanes, apart from the fluorosilanes, lies in their use as reaction intermediates for preparing other silicon compounds. This matter will be considered in the next sections, but here it is worth mentioning the compounds obtained by treating silver cyanide or silver thiocyanate with silyl iodide, SiH_3I.[213] The compound from silver cyanide and silyl iodide melts at 32.4° and boils at 49.6°/760 mm. Since, as has long been known, methyl iodide and silver cyanide yield methyl *iso*cyanide,[132] by analogy it was suggested[213] that the compound obtained from silyl iodide was also the *iso*-derivative. However, the infrared spectra of the products from the $AgCN-SiH_3I$ and the $AgCN-SiD_3I$ reactions have been studied, and the observed isotopic shifts produced by ^{13}C and ^{15}N in the CN stretching mode of SiD_3CN strongly suggest that the compound has a normal cyanide rather than an *iso*cyanide structure.[205,206] This has been confirmed by a study of the microwave spectrum.[229a,278] The compound obtained by passing silyl iodide over silver thiocyanate,[213] on the other hand, has been shown by a study of its microwave spectrum to be silyl *iso*thiocyanate (Table 2) rather than silyl thiocyanate.[161] This conclusion was suggested earlier after examination of the infrared spectrum indicated that the molecule is a symmetric top with Si, N, C, and S atoms linear.[215] Linearity implies nitrogen-silicon $p_\pi-d_\pi$ bonding, $H_3Si=N=C=S$, like that in trisilylamine, described below.

The compound SiH_3CN reacts with diborane to give a solid material formulated as SiH_3CN, BH_3, which on heating releases silane forming $(BH_2CN)_x$ polymer.[103] Boron halides react with silyl cyanide at low temperatures to form unstable addition compounds which decompose on warming to room temperature with transfer of halogen from boron to silicon.[104]

$$SiH_3CN + BX_3 \longrightarrow H_3SiCN,BX_3 \longrightarrow SiH_3X + \frac{1}{x}(BX_2CN)_x$$
$$(X = F, Cl)$$

2. COMPOUNDS WITH ELEMENTS OF THE Vth GROUP

The compound trisilylamine, $(SiH_3)_3N$, spontaneously inflammable in air and vigorously decomposed by water, was first obtained by Stock and his co-workers[293] from the reaction between excess of silyl chloride and ammonia. It was believed that in this reaction the hypothetical amines SiH_3NH_2 and $(SiH_3)_2NH$ rapidly disproportionated to form ammonia and

trisilylamine.   Furthermore, it was subsequently noted[48] that for a good
yield of trisilylamine it was necessary to add gaseous ammonia to gaseous
silyl chloride.   If this procedure is not followed silane and polymeric
$(SiH_2NH)_x$ are formed in relatively large amounts.   The amminolysis of
silyl chloride has recently been reinvestigated with very interesting
results.[265a]   The novel heterocyclic silicon compound $(SiH_3NSiH_2)_3$ can
be isolated from the reaction between silyl chloride and ammonia by
warming the reactants, in the ratio 3:4, from $-196°$ to ambient temperatures.   Trisilylamine and silane are also produced.   Moreover, it was
found that N,N′,N″-trisilylcyclotrisilazane (Table 3) is also formed by
treating liquid trisilylamine with liquid ammonia; silane and non-volatile
materials being obtained simultaneously.   However, trisilylamine does
not react with ammonia *in the gas phase* even at 100°.   This study has
cast new light on the formation of trisilylamine from silyl chloride and
ammonia.   The high yields of trisilylamine obtained when silyl chloride
and ammonia are brought together in the gas phase are understandable
since secondary decomposition is avoided, because ammonia and trisilylamine do not react in the gas phase.   Furthermore, the production of
silane and non-volatile products in the amminolysis of silyl halides can
now be explained on a basis other than decomposition of hypothetical
lower amines.

In the liquid-phase reaction between trisilylamine and ammonia,
analysis of reactants and products showed that the ammonia could be
recovered if the process was stopped after a short time.

$$xNH_3 + 3(SiH_3)_3N \longrightarrow (SiH_3NSiH_2)_3 + 3SiH_4 + xNH_3$$

Reactions between ND_3 and $(SiH_3)_3N$, or between NH_3 and $(SiD_3)_3N$,
showed that hydrogen atoms from ammonia are not included in the silane
formed.   If reaction was allowed to occur between ammonia and trisilylamine for an extended time period, ammonia could not be recovered and
non-volatile materials were produced.   The ammonia catalyzed elimination of silane from trisilylamine was also observed with other bases (trimethylamine, methylamine, lithium hydride), the trisilylamine behaving
as an acceptor molecule presumably *via* employment of silicon 3d orbitals.
The tendency for trisilylamine to function as a weak Lewis base is described below.   Consequently, trisilylamine can be regarded as displaying
amphoteric character.

N,N′,N″-trisilylcyclotrisilazane reacts with ammonia to give silane and non-volatile material, and with excess of hydrogen chloride at or below room temperature to afford silyl chloride and dichlorosilane.[265a] In the hydrogen chloride reaction, cleavage of SiH_3 groups was quantitative, but the quantity of dichlorosilane formed was somewhat less than that predicted by the equation,

$$(SiH_3NSiH_2)_3 + 12HCl \longrightarrow 3NH_4Cl + 3SiH_2Cl_2 + 3SiH_3Cl$$

a reaction analogous to the quantitative process

$$(SiH_3)_3N + 4HCl \longrightarrow 3SiH_3Cl + NH_4Cl \tag{293}$$

The slow and incomplete formation of dichlorosilane from trisilylcyclotrisilazane suggested that the latter compound might react with a deficiency of hydrogen chloride to yield an unsubstituted cyclotrisilazane. In this manner a very small quantity of material (B.P. 89.0°, extrap.) tentatively assigned the formula $(SiH_2NH)_3$ was obtained. Further information on the chemistry of the cyclotrisilazanes will be awaited with great interest.

Treatment of SiH_3Cl or SiH_3Br with methylamines yields mixed compounds like $(SiH_3)_2NCH_3$,[92,306] viz.

$$nSiH_3X + (n + 1)(CH_3)_{3-n}NH_n = (CH_3)_{3-n}(SiH_3)_nN + n(CH_3)_{3-n}NH_nHX$$

The compound $(SiH_3)_2NC_2H_5$ has also been described.[92] Hydrogen halides cleave the silicon—nitrogen bonds in these amines to yield SiH_3X. Quaternary ammonium salts containing SiH_3 groups are not formed. The compound $(CH_3)_2NSiH_3$, unlike the other silylamines, decomposes even in the gas phase above its M.P. of 3.4°. This melting point is relatively high compared with the melting points of other silylamines (Table 3), and this and other properties have led to the suggestion that the solid is polymerized to some extent by virtue of intermolecular $N \rightarrow Si$ dative bonding, made possible by the ability of silicon to expand its valence shell.

The previously mentioned iodide, Si_2H_5I, reacts rapidly with ammonia to give good yields of tris-disilanylamine, $(Si_2H_5)_3N$, a liquid spontaneously inflammable in air but thermally stable at about 100° for several hours.[328]

The silylamines react with a number of boron compounds. These reactions have clearly demonstrated differences in behaviour between

TABLE 3. SOME SILYL DERIVATIVES OF Vth GROUP ELEMENTS.

Compound	M.P.	B.P.	Reference	Compound	M.P.	B.P.	Reference
$(SiH_3)_3N$	−105.6°	52°	293	$(CH_3)_2N(SiH_2CH_3)$	...	86.2°	80
$(SiH_3)_2NCH_3$	−124.1°	32.3°	92,306	$CH_3N(SiH_2CH_3)_2$	−115°	80.1°	80
$SiH_3N(CH_3)_2$	3.4°	...	306	$(CH_3SiH_2)_3N$	−107°	108.6°	80
$(SiH_3)_2NC_2H_5$	−127°	65.9°	92	$(SiH_3)_2NB_2H_5$	−69°	54°	48
$SiH_2[N(CH_3)_2]_2$	−104°	93°	12	$(SiH_3)(CH_3)NB_2H_5$	−39.0°	51°	48
$SiH[N(CH_3)_2]_3$	−90°	144°	12	SiH_3PI_2	−1.8°	190°	15
$(Si_2H_5)_3N$	−97.1°	178.8°	328	SiH_3AsI_2	−4.0°	210°	15
$(SiH_3NSiH_2)_3$	...	133.0°	265a	$(SiH_3)_2NN(SiH_3)_2$	...	109°	11
$(SiH_3)_2NCN$	−74.8°	84.7°	81a	...	...	...	...

aliphatic amines and silylamines, caused chiefly by the ability of silicon to use bonding orbitals above the $3s3p$ level.

The weak electron donor properties of trisilylamine were recognized first by Stock,[293] and later workers[48] showed that $(SiH_3)_3N$ does not bond BH_3 or $B(CH_3)_3$. This is in contrast to the existence of the stable compounds $(CH_3)_3N \cdot BH_3$ and $(CH_3)_3N \cdot B(CH_3)_3$. Furthermore, unlike the very stable adduct $(CH_3)_3N \cdot BF_3$, $(SiH_3)_3N \cdot BF_3$ forms only well below room temperature. With boron trichloride at $-78°$ trisilylamine gives a solid formulated as $(SiH_3)_3N \cdot BCl_3$, but even at this temperature the complex forms SiH_3Cl and $(SiH_3)_2NBCl_2$. The latter substance polymerizes on standing, like $(CH_3)_2NBCl_2$, and decomposes above $60°$ releasing hydrogen, SiH_4, SiH_3Cl and SiH_2Cl_2, and forming a glassy residue. With bromodiborane, trisilylamine forms N,N,-bis-silylaminoborane.

$$2(SiH_3)_3N + 2B_2H_5Br \longrightarrow 2SiH_3Br + B_2H_6 + 2(SiH_3)_2NBH_2$$

Bis-silylaminoborane is similar to many other aminoboron compounds existing partly as a dimer and partly as a monomer. The monomeric form reacts with diborane to form N,N-bis-silylaminodiborane, $(SiH_3)_2NB_2H_5$, differing from the corresponding carbon analogues $R_2NB_2H_5$ in its spontaneous inflammability and in its ease of thermal decomposition.[48,298] Treatment of $CH_3N(SiH_3)_2$ with B_2H_5Br affords the thermally more stable but spontaneously inflammable $(CH_3NSiH_3)B_2H_5$.

On the Pauling scale the electronegativity of carbon is 2.5 and that of silicon is 1.8. On the basis of such simple electronegativity considerations, it would be expected that trisilylamine would be a stronger electron-pair donor than trimethylamine, yet $(SiH_3)_3N$ forms no complexes or only weak complexes with Lewis acids derived from boron. This led A. B. Burg[48] to suggest that the lone pair of electrons on the nitrogen atom in $(SiH_3)_3N$ is involved in internal dative bonding from nitrogen to the vacant $3d$-orbitals of the silicon atoms. The existence of such Si—N d_π—p_π bonding would render trisilylamine a weak donor, since in order to bond an acceptor moiety an appreciable energy of rehybridization would be required to convert the nitrogen atom in $(SiH_3)_3N$ towards the sp^3 configuration found in the addition compound. Rehybridization energy[297] would be much lower in trimethylamine where the bond angles are such that it may be assumed that the nitrogen atom in the free base is already in essentially an sp^3 configuration.   If the nitrogen lone pair in $(SiH_3)_3N$ engages in double bonding with the silicon atoms, the silylamine will assume a different structure from the pyramidal one of trimethyl-amine.   The more extensive the d_π—p_π bonding in $(SiH_3)_3N$ the more it would be expected that the three silicon atoms and the nitrogen atom would tend to be coplanar.   Following A. B. Burg's suggestion, an electron diffraction study was made on trisilylamine by Hedberg[154] who found that the Si_3N skeleton was indeed planar.

An attempt has been made to measure the change in Lewis base strength as silyl groups in $(SiH_3)_3N$ are replaced by methyl. This has been tried using both trimethylboron and boron trifluoride as reference Lewis acids.   However, in the series $(SiH_3)_3N$, $(SiH_3)_2NCH_3$, $SiH_3N(CH_3)_2$, $(CH_3)_3N$ only the last two compounds form adducts with trimethylboron, and of these $(SiH_3)(CH_3)_2N \cdot B(CH_3)_3$ is completely dissociated in the gas phase, rendering any quantitative determination of the N—B dative bond strength impossible.[306]   Nevertheless, on the basis of other properties it has been *estimated*[306] that the N—B dative bond strength in $(SiH_3)(CH_3)_2N \cdot B(CH_3)_3$ is about 8.5 kcal., which is to be compared with that of 17.6 kcal. *measured* for $(CH_3)_3N \cdot B(CH_3)_3$.[44] When the base strength of the above series of amines was compared using boron trifluoride as the reference Lewis acid, all the silylamines absorbed an equimolar quantity of the acid, but then a secondary reaction occurred yielding silyl fluoride and aminoboron difluorides,[307] e.g.,

$$(SiH_3)_3N + BF_3 \longrightarrow (SiH_3)_3N \cdot BF_3 \longrightarrow SiH_3F + (SiH_3)_2NBF_2$$

Disilylaminoboron difluoride (vapor pressure 13.2 mm./−49.3°) decomposes slowly at room temperature yielding SiH_3F and a material which is very probably the borazole $(SiH_3NBF)_3$.

The structure of trisilylamine and its chemical behavior would appear to provide irrefutable evidence in support of the idea that silicon can use orbitals above the sp^3 level, provided certain conditions are met, *viz.*, that silicon be bonded to an electronegative atom or group possessing π-electrons or electrons which can acquire π-symmetry.

Whereas the di- and tri-halosilanes react with ammonia to give ammonium chloride and polymeric materials with Si—N bonds, dimethylamine, where only one protonic hydrogen is linked to the donor atom, reacts with diiodosilane to give $SiH_2[N(CH_3)_2]_2$ and with trichloro-silane to give $SiH[N(CH_3)_2]_3$.[12]

The silylamines mentioned above were derived from silyl halides. Further examples of the use of these halides to create bonds between silicon and nitrogen are the formation of $N_2(SiH_3)_4$ from silyl iodide and anhydrous hydrazine,[11] and the formation of $(SiH_3)_2NCN$ from silyl iodide and silver cyanamide.[81a] The compound tetrasilylhydrazine (Table 3) is explosively oxidized by air, but is stable *in vacuo* to 90°. Like trisilylamine, tetrasilylhydrazine has a noticeable lack of donor power. The infrared and Raman spectra of tetrasilylhydrazine have been recorded, as discussed in a later section.

From the direct reaction between silane and phosphine at from 450-500° it is possible to prepare silylphosphine, SiH_3PH_2.[115] This compound is a liquid at ambient temperatures, is spontaneously inflammable in air, and possesses strong reducing properties. The silicon—phosphorus bond is broken by hydroxide, alkoxide or amide ions to give phosphine and SiH_3R, where R = OH, OC_2H_5, or NH_2. Then the SiH_3R moiety produced reacts with solvent to give hydrogen and SiR_4 except in the case of SiH_3NH_2 which gives SiH_4 and polymeric $(SiH_2NH)_x$.[119]

Silyl iodide reacts with phosphorus at temperatures between 20° and 100° to yield SiH_3PI_2, $(SiH_3)_2PI$ and $(SiH_3)_3P$, as well as SiH_2I_2 and SiH_4, disproportionation products of SiH_3I.[15] Of the silylphosphorus compounds only SiH_3PI_2 has been obtained in a pure state since $(SiH_3)_2PI$ has a similar volatility to SiH_2I_2, and $(SiH_3)_3P$ a similar volatility to SiH_3I. The reaction between silyl iodide and arsenic gives similar products, but the only silylarsenic compound which has been obtained pure is SiH_3AsI_2. The compounds SiH_3PI_2 and SiH_3AsI_2 decompose slowly at ambient temperatures into hydrogen, hydrogen iodide, silyl iodide and phosphine or arsine. At elevated temperatures silyldiiodo-phosphine and -arsine decompose rapidly.

3. COMPOUNDS WITH ELEMENTS OF THE VIth GROUP

The compound disiloxane, $(SiH_3)_2O$, the silicon analogue of dimethyl ether, is formed by the hydrolysis of many compounds containing the SiH_3 group, e.g.,

$$2SiH_3I + H_2O \longrightarrow 2HI + (SiH_3)_2O \qquad (89)$$

Disiloxane, which probably forms through condensation of the intermediate SiH_3OH, was characterized first by Stock and his co-workers,[293] who found that the compound will burn in air when ignited but that it is not spontaneously inflammable. It reacts vigorously with chlorine even at low temperatures to give a mixture of $SiCl_4$ and $(SiCl_3)_2O$. Thermally it is comparatively stable since it has been heated to over 300° without appreciable decomposition. The related compound silyl methyl ether has been prepared *via* the reaction,[290a]

$$(CH_3)_3N, SiH_3I + CH_3OH \longrightarrow SiH_3OCH_3 + [(CH_3)_3NH]I$$

Silyl methyl ether is stable at room temperature. In the presence of copper metal the compound releases hydrogen, and it is quantitatively hydrolyzed by water according to the equation,

$$2SiH_3OCH_3 + H_2O \longrightarrow (SiH_3)_2O + 2CH_3OH$$

Silyl methyl ether is also decomposed by iodine forming silyl iodide. Disiloxane behaves similarly, as described below. Recently the compound $(SiH_3SiH_2)_2O$ has been characterized having been obtained *via* the reaction,[327]

$$2SiH_3SiH_2I + H_2O \longrightarrow (SiH_3SiH_2)_2O + 2HI$$

This compound, the silicon analogue of diethyl ether, is thermally more stable than the iodide Si_2H_5I from which it is derived.

Disilyl sulfide has been prepared in yields of over 90% by passing silyl iodide over mercury(II) sulfide at ordinary temperatures.[89] The reaction is exothermic. The compound $(Si_2H_5)_2S$ may be made from the iodide Si_2H_5I and HgS.[328] Although silyl iodide does not react with mercury(II) selenide even up to temperatures of 75°, the compound disilyl selenide may be obtained in about 60% yield by passing SiH_3I over silver selenide.* Disilyl sulfide and selenide react with water to form disiloxane, and all the silyl derivatives of the Group VI elements release hydrogen

---

* A "Conversion Series" may be used to predict whether a particular compound containing an SiH_3 group will react with a particular silver salt.[214] Reaction between a specific compound and a silver salt will afford any compound later in the series but none earlier therein:

$$SiH_3I \longrightarrow (SiH_3)_2Se \longrightarrow (SiH_3)_2S \longrightarrow SiH_3Br \longrightarrow SiH_3CN \longrightarrow$$
$$SiH_3Cl \longrightarrow SiH_3NCS \longrightarrow SiH_3CNO \longrightarrow (SiH_3)_2O \longrightarrow SiH_3F$$

when treated with aqueous alkali. Disilyl sulfide is slowly decomposed when held at 100°, while the selenide decomposes slightly at its boiling point. Other reactions of these compounds (Table 4) may be summarized by the equations,[89,214]

$$(SiH_3)_2M + I_2 \longrightarrow 2SiH_3I + M$$
$$(M = O, S, \text{ or } Se)$$

$$(SiH_3)_2M + 2HI \longrightarrow 2SiH_3I + H_2M$$
$$(M = S, \text{ or } Se)$$

$$(SiH_3)_2S + HgCl_2 \longrightarrow 2SiH_3Cl + HgS$$

$$2(SiH_3)_2O + (CH_3)_4Al_2Br_2 \longrightarrow [(CH_3)_2AlOSiH_3]_2 + 2SiH_3Br$$

$$SiH_3OCH_3 + BF_3 \longrightarrow SiH_3F + CH_3OBF_2$$

$$(SiH_3)_2O + BCl_3 \longrightarrow SiH_3Cl + SiH_3OBCl_2$$

The last reaction is reminiscent of that between boron trichloride and trisilylamine, mentioned above. Although the dimeric compound $[(CH_3)_2AlOSiH_3]_2$ has been described[189] as being electron deficient, because the Al—O—Al bridge bonds are of the normal electron pair type, use of the term electron deficient[299] in this instance is not appropriate.

Failure of these silyl derivatives to form oxonium, sulfonium or selenonium type compounds indicates that they are much weaker electron pair donors than their methyl analogues. Indeed, it was predicted[300] that disiloxane and disilyl sulfide would have no Lewis base properties shortly before a detailed report of the chemistry of these compounds appeared.[89] It is to be expected that in disiloxane and disilyl sulfide d_π—p_π bonding would occur to a certain extent by analogy with the situation existing in trisilylamine, discussed above. In the oxygen and sulfur compounds the conditions for π-bonding are present, i.e., electronegative donor atoms possessing electrons which can acquire π-symmetry are bonded to an atom having vacant orbitals, in this case the silicon $3d$. However, it must not be thought from this that π-bonding in $(SiH_3)_2O$ or $(SiH_3)_2S$ is likely to be so important as it is in $(SiH_3)_3N$. Many observations have been made showing that donor power decreases in the sequence $N > P > O > S$ towards the proton and towards most Lewis acids of the Group III elements, e.g., BF_3. Therefore, if the reasonable assumption is made that the capacity of a donor atom for forming internal dative bonds follows its capacity for forming normal coordinate bonds,

TABLE 4. SILYL DERIVATIVES OF VIth GROUP ELEMENTS.

Compound	M.P.	B.P.	Reference	Compound	M.P.	B.P.	Reference
$(SiH_3)_2O$	$-144°$	$-15.2°$	293	SiH_3SCF_3	$-127°$	$13.6°$	75
$(SiH_3)_2S$	$-70.0°$	$58.8°$	89	$SiH_3SC_2H_5$	....	$15-20°/0.1$ mm	269
$(SiH_3)_2Se$	$-68.0°$	$85.2°$	89	$(CH_3SiH_2)_2O$	$-138°$	$34.5°$	94
SiH_3SH	$-124°$	$14.2°$	89	$[(CH_3)_2SiH]_2O$	....	$73°$	97
SiH_3OCH_3	$-98.5°$	$-21.1°$	290a	$(CH_3SiH_2)_2S$	$-120°$	$105°$	94
$H_2Si(OCH_3)_2$	$-99.8°$	$33.5°$	290	$[(CH_3)_2SiH]_2S$	$-146°$	$145°$	97
$HSi(OCH_3)_3$	$-114.8°$	$81.1°$	290	$(Si_2H_5)_2O$	....	$94.8°$	327
....	....	....	....	$(Si_2H_5)_2S$	$-70.4°$	$143.8°$	328

it is to be expected that d_π—p_π bonding would be less extensive in disiloxane and very much less extensive in disilyl sulfide than it is in trisilylamine. On the basis of simple electronegativity considerations it is to be expected that $(SiH_3)_2O$ and $(SiH_3)_2S$ would be stronger Lewis bases than their carbon analogues. Since this is not so, it is reasonable to assume that d_π—p_π bonding is playing some part in the ground states of these compounds. If this is true, it should affect the structures of $(SiH_3)_2O$ and $(SiH_3)_2S$. From the above remarks concerning internal dative bonding power, it is to be anticipated[300] that the Si—O—Si bond angle in $(SiH_3)_2O$ would be much larger than the C—O—C angle in aliphatic ethers, but that the Si—S—Si bond angle in $(SiH_3)_2S$ would be perhaps only a little larger than the C—S—C angle in aliphatic sulfides. In $(CH_3)_2O$ the C—O—C bond angle is 111°, while in $(CH_3)_2S$ the C—S—C angle is 105°. These bond angles are within the range expected when the central atom is using bonding orbitals formed by mixing s and p orbitals. In these carbon compounds d_π—p_π bonding cannot occur because carbon has no vacant orbitals above the $2s2p$ level suitable for use in chemical bonding. Several infrared spectral studies[59,210] have been made and an electron diffraction investigation[105] carried out on disiloxane. From the results obtained, it is certain that the Si—O—Si angle is far greater than 110°, providing strong evidence for the existence of silicon-oxygen d_π—p_π bonding, but as described in a later section there has been considerable argument as to the actual magnitude of the angle in question. Two infrared spectra studies[84,204] have been made on disilyl sulfide and the results of one of these[204] have been interpreted in terms of a Si—S—Si angle of about 100°. If this estimate of the angle is correct, there would appear to be very little silicon-sulfur π-bonding in this molecule. It is rather surprising, therefore, that disilyl sulfide does not form sulphonium compounds like its carbon analogue.[89]

Thus, in terms of chemical reactions and structural considerations, evidence points to π-bonding, using the silicon $3d$ orbitals, decreasing along the series $(SiH_3)_3N$, $(SiH_3)_2O$, $(SiH_3)_2S$ in accordance with expectations.

One further piece of experimental work in this area is of interest. Trisilylamine forms no compound with trimethylgallium under a variety of conditions, but from temperature-composition curves it appears that disiloxane and trimethylgallium do form a one-to-one adduct at low temperatures.[305]   This behavior is contrary to the rule mentioned earlier that towards Group III acceptors nitrogen is a better donor than oxygen, but it is in accord with the idea[305] that silicon-oxygen π-bonding in $(SiH_3)_2O$ is less than the silicon-nitrogen π-bonding in $(SiH_3)_3N$.   This follows from a consideration of the energetics of addition compound formation[297] where an important energy term is the shaping of the donor and acceptor moieties to the configurations found in the final product.   The fact that towards a reference acid disiloxane forms an adduct whereas trisilylamine does not implies that less rehybridization energy is required in addition compound formation by disiloxane than by trisilylamine. Since rehybridization energy of these bases will decrease as the d_π—p_π bonding decreases, the results[305] suggest less π-bonding in $(SiH_3)_2O$ than in $(SiH_3)_3N$.

It is interesting that in the formation of molecular addition compounds rehybridization considerations are usually far more important for the Lewis acid moiety than for the base.[297]   These silyl compounds are examples of the comparatively rare situation where the base has to undergo a drastic change in shape in adduct formation.

In addition to disilyl sulfide it has been possible to prepare three other compounds in which a silyl group is bonded to sulfur.   These are silylethyl sulfide, silyl mercaptan and silyl trifluoromethyl sulfide.   Silyl mercaptan (SiH_3SH) is formed when disilyl sulfide and hydrogen sulfide are mixed at room temperatures.[89]   This is an equilibrium reaction since silyl mercaptan begins to decompose slowly even at $-78°$ to produce disilyl sulfide and hydrogen sulfide.   Compounds having a silyl group and a hydrogen atom bonded to a central atom often undergo a condensation reaction, e.g.,

$$2SiH_3SH \longrightarrow (SiH_3)_2S + H_2S$$
$$3SiH_3NH_2 \longrightarrow (SiH_3)_3N + 2NH_3$$
$$2SiH_3OH \longrightarrow (SiH_3)_2O + H_2O$$

In some cases these reactions are so rapid that the starting compound has only a transitory existence, decomposing as soon as it is formed.   However, the last two reactions are hypothetical, and as mentioned on page 28 it is not certain that SiH_3NH_2 is an intermediate in the formation of trisilylamine.

The compound $SiH_3SC_2H_5$ has been prepared by reducing $Cl_3SiSC_2H_5$ with lithium aluminum hydride.[269]

Silyl trifluoromethyl sulfide has been prepared by treating solid bis-(trifluoromethylthio)mercury with silyl iodide vapor.[75] The compound is stable when pure at room temperature in a clean glass apparatus. Decomposition, however, *via* the reaction

$$SiH_3SCF_3 \longrightarrow SiH_3F + SCF_2$$

is catalysed by bis(trifluoromethylthio)mercury, and in dirty apparatus occurs even at $-46°$. Hydrogen iodide breaks the silicon—sulfur bond giving silyl iodide and trifluoromethylthiol. Reaction with trimethyl-amine has been represented by the equation

$$SiH_3SCF_3 + 2(CH_3)_3N \longrightarrow (CH_3)_3N,SiH_3F + (CH_3)_3NSCF_2$$

This reaction is very similar to,

$$(SiH_3)_2S + (CH_3)_3N \longrightarrow SiH_4 + (CH_3)_3NSSiH_2$$

4. ORGANOSILICON HYDRIDES R_nSiH_{4-n} (n = 1, 2, 3)

The three main synthetic routes used to prepare compounds of the type $RSiH_3$, R_2SiH_2, and R_3SiH involve (1) reduction of an organohalosilane or an organoalkoxysilane with a metal hydride or complex metal hydride, (2) addition of a silane, e.g., SiH_4, $RSiH_3$, or R_2SiH_2, to a carbon—carbon double or triple bond, and (3) by the action of an organometallic compound, usually a Grignard reagent, on a halosilane. The first method has been reviewed earlier, and will not be discussed further here.

Creation of Si—C bonds by addition of Si—H bonds to olefins or acetylenes was mentioned earlier, when the reaction between silane and ethylene was discussed. This type of reaction, discovered two decades ago, has become one of the most important in organosilicon chemistry with the result that the technical literature pertaining to the reaction has become very large, so that a detailed account of the subject would be beyond the scope of what is intended for this volume. In brief, the addition reaction is characterized by the large number of unsaturated carbon compounds and compounds containing Si—H bonds which are known to undergo it, and by the wide variety of conditions of pressure, heat or catalysis which has been employed.* The best reaction con-

---

* For a comprehensive review see references 78 and 133.

ditions generally involve use of catalysts (e.g., peroxides, tertiary bases, metals or metal salts) or irradiation with ultraviolet light or γ-rays.

The peroxide and radiation-induced additions involve free radical processes like those that occur between halogenomethanes and olefins. Thermal addition of silanes to olefins probably also involves radicals and chain processes but it is possible that some of the thermal reactions are bimolecular in character. Reactions between silicon hydrides and C=C or C≡C groups which are catalysed by palladium or potassium chloroplatinate are complex in nature and the mechanism of addition is probably ionic.

In order to obtain an organosilicon *hydride*, rather than a tetra-organosilicon compound, from a reaction between an unsaturated carbon compound and a silane, it is obviously necessary that the silicon compound contain more than one Si—H bond per molecule, and that the conditions be such that reaction stops before all product is in the form of a tetra-organosilicon derivative.* Some typical reactions which have given organosilanes are,

$$C_6H_5SiH_3 + CH_2:CHCH_2N[Si(CH_3)_3]_2 \xrightarrow{\text{peroxide}}$$
$$C_6H_5H_2Si(CH_2)_3N[Si(CH_3)_3]_2 \qquad (286)$$

$$C_6H_5SiH_3 + CH_2:CH(CH_2)_5CH_3 \xrightarrow{\text{peroxide}}$$
$$C_6H_5H_2Si(n\text{-}C_8H_{17}) + C_6H_5HSi(n\text{-}C_8H_{17})_2 \qquad (286)$$

$$(CH_3)_2SiH_2 + CF_2:CF_2 \xrightarrow{\text{u.v.}} (CH_3)_2HSiCF_2CF_2H + (CH_3)_2HSi(CF_2CF_2)_nH + (CH_3)_2Si(CF_2CF_2H)_2 \qquad (134)$$

$$(C_2H_5)_2SiH_2 + CH_2:CH(CH_2)_6CH_3 \xrightarrow{\text{Pt}} (C_2H_5)_2HSi(n\text{-}C_9H_{19}) \qquad (317)$$

Synthesis of organosilicon hydrides by treating halosilanes with organometallic reagents is important because it was the first method used to make organosilanes, and because it is still used to make these compounds. Thus in 1919 Stock and Somieski[294] prepared the first known dialkylsilane, $(CH_3)_2SiH_2$, by treating dichlorosilane with dimethylzinc, and in 1884 Pape[244] claimed tripropylsilane from the reaction between

---

* The addition reaction is usually carried out with the express purpose of obtaining a tetraorganosilicon compound, and frequently to obtain an organofunctional silicon derivative.

trichlorosilane and dipropylzinc. The discovery that $SiHCl_3$ and SiH_2Cl_2 can be obtained directly from silicon or certain silicides has led to a wide use of these compounds as intermediates for preparing R_3SiH and R_2SiH_2 compounds. The following reactions are examples of this procedure:

$$C_2H_5MgBr + HSiCl_3 \longrightarrow (C_2H_5)_3SiH \qquad (187)$$

$$CH_2:CHCH_2MgBr + HSiCl_3 \longrightarrow (CH_2:CHCH_2)_3SiH \qquad (162)$$

$$n\text{-}C_4H_9MgCl + HSiCl_3 \longrightarrow (n\text{-}C_4H_9)_3SiH \qquad (163)$$

$$C_6H_{11}MgBr + H_2SiCl_2 \longrightarrow (C_6H_{11})_2SiH_2 \qquad (333)$$

By treating trichlorosilane with a deficiency of chloro-Grignard, mixed organohalosilanes have been obtained, e.g., $(n\text{-}C_4H_9)_2SiHCl$,[163] $(C_6H_5)_2SiHCl$.[96]* It has also been possible to prepare mixed organosilanes, e.g., $(CH_3)_2(n\text{-}C_3H_7)SiH$, from the simultaneous reaction of trichlorosilane with two Grignard reagents.[256]

Organolithium compounds have also been employed in reactions of this type, e.g.,

$$3(CH_3)_3SiCH_2Li + SiHCl_3 \longrightarrow [(CH_3)_3SiCH_2]_3SiH + 3LiCl \qquad (62)$$

As mentioned earlier in this chapter, silyl bromide can be made in quantity from silane,[238] so this halide has been used to make organosilanes of the type $RSiH_3$ by means of the Grignard reagent:

$$SiH_3Br + n\text{-}C_3H_7MgBr \longrightarrow n\text{-}C_3H_7SiH_3 + MgBr_2 \qquad (238)$$

$$2SiH_3Br + BrMgC_2MgBr \longrightarrow H_3SiC:CSiH_3 + 2MgBr_2 \qquad (209, 233)$$

Organosilanes show in some degree all the characteristic reactions expected of molecules containing Si—H bonds, but as would be anticipated, the vigor of these reactions decreases along the series $RSiH_3$, R_2SiH_2, R_3SiH.

Unlike the parent silanes, the organosilanes are not spontaneously inflammable in air under normal conditions. They are, however, fairly easily oxidized and their spontaneous ignition temperatures decrease with decreasing substitution of hydrogen on silicon by organo-groups. This is

---

* Organohalosilanes can sometimes be obtained directly from silicon. Thus CH_3SiHCl_2 can be prepared on a large scale by passing a mixture of methyl chloride and hydrogen over heated silicon activated by copper.[22]

TABLE 5. SOME ORGANOSILANES.*

Compound	M.P.	B.P.	Reference	Compound	M.P.	B.P.	Reference
CH_3SiH_3	−156.8°	−57.5°	312	$C_2H_5SiH_3$	−179.7°	−13.7°	312
$(CH_3)_2SiH_2$	−150.2°	−19.6°	312	$(C_2H_5)_2SiH_2$	−134.4°	56°	312
$(CH_3)_3SiH$	−135.9°	6.7°	312	$(C_2H_5)_3SiH$	−156.9°	108.8°	312
n-$C_3H_7SiH_3$	...	23°	111	...	...	...	
$(n$-$C_3H_7)_2SiH_2$	...	111°	111	$(i$-$C_3H_7)_2SiH_2$	...	98.5°/778 mm	333
$(n$-$C_3H_7)_3SiH$	...	169.5°	256	$(i$-$C_3H_7)_3SiH$	...	60°/10 mm	247
$C_6H_5SiH_3$	...	120°	111	$CH_2{:}CHSiH_3$	−179.1 α, −171.6 β	−22.8°	312
$(C_6H_5)_2SiH_2$	...	95-97°/13 mm	333	$(CH_2{:}CH)_3SiH$	...	92.5°	259
$(C_6H_5)_3SiH$	...	152-167°/2 mm	142	$(CH_2{:}CHCH_2)_3SiH$	...	160-165°/760 mm	162
$H_3Si(CH_2)SiH_3$	...	14.7°/754 mm	101,248	$H_3SiC{:}CSiH_3$	−59°	43°	233
$H_3Si(CH_2)_2SiH_3$	...	46°/747 mm	101,248				
$H_3Si(CH_2)_3SiH_3$	...	77.9°/757 mm	248	$(C_2H_5)_2SiHCl$	−143°	99.7°	223
CH_3SiHF_2	−110°	−35.6°	32	$C_2H_5SiHCl_2$	−107°	74.9°	223
CH_3SiH_2Cl	−134.5°	7°	293	n-$C_4H_9SiHCl_2$	...	129°	223
CH_3SiHCl_2	−92.5°	40.7°	263	$C_6H_5SiHCl_2$	...	184°	199
$CH_3SiHFCl$	−120.2°	1.2°	32	$(C_6H_5)_2SiHCl$	...	143°/10 mm	20
$CH_2{:}CHSiHCl_2$	...	66.5°	302				
$(C_6H_5CH_2)(CH_3)SiHCl$	...	76-83°/6 mm	163				
CH_3SiH_2Br	−119°	34°	80	$C_6H_5SiH_2Br$	−30°	118°/70 mm	224
$C_2H_5SiHBr_2$	...	120°	193				
CH_3SiH_2I	−109.5°	71.8°	336	$(CH_3)_2SiHI$	−88°	92°	97

* The compounds given in this table are representative. Many other organosilanes are known. For a comprehensive treatment of these compounds, the reader is referred to Gmelins Handbuch der Anorganischen Chemie, Silicium (1958), and to "Organosilicon Compounds," C. Eaborn, Butterworths, 1960.

very marked in the methyl- and ethylsilanes,[148,267] less pronounced in the
n-propyl series, and still less pronounced in the n-butyl and n-amyl series.

Although hydrogen is the only volatile product when silane is treated
with active nitrogen, with the methylsilanes, hydrogen cyanide and
ammonia are produced in addition to hydrogen.[70]

Some or all of the hydrogen atoms in the alkylsilanes may be replaced
by halogen using reactions analogous to those employed for the halogenation of the parent silanes:

$$2CH_3SiH_3 + 3HI \xrightarrow[100°]{AlI_3} CH_3SiH_2I + CH_3SiHI_2 + 3H_2 \qquad (94)$$

$$(C_2H_5)_3SiH + RCl \xrightarrow{AlCl_3} (C_2H_5)_3SiCl + RH \qquad (336)$$

$$3(C_2H_5)_3SiH + 2(C_2H_5)_2SiCl_2 \xrightarrow{AlCl_3} 3(C_2H_5)_3SiCl + (C_2H_5)_2SiHCl$$
$$+ (C_2H_5)_2SiH_2 \qquad (336)$$

$$3(C_2H_5)_3SiH + n\text{-}C_4H_9SiCl_3 \xrightarrow{AlCl_3} 3(C_2H_5)_3SiCl + n\text{-}C_4H_9SiH_3 \qquad (36)$$

The last three equations represent reactions reminiscent of those
described earlier between Si_3H_8 and chloroform, and between SiH_4 and
dichlorosilane.

Direct halogenation of organosilanes proceeds much more mildly
than with the parent silanes. Bromination of triphenylsilane, for example, takes place only slowly in refluxing carbon tetrachloride.[24] Organosilicon iodides are formed in a smooth reaction between triorganosilanes
and iodine.[64,326] In contrast, treatment of a phenyliodosilane with
iodine leads to silicon—carbon bond cleavage by the hydrogen iodide
produced in the iodination step, e.g.,[124]

$$C_6H_5SiH_2I + I_2 \longrightarrow C_6H_5SiHI_2 + HI$$
$$C_6H_5SiH_2I + HI \longrightarrow C_6H_6 + SiH_2I_2$$
$$SiH_2I_2 + 2I_2 \longrightarrow SiI_4 + 2HI$$

Chlorine or bromine, on the other hand, easily reacts with phenylsilane
to give phenyltrihalosilanes, no silicon—phenyl bond cleavage occurring.[125a]

The reader is reminded that cleavage of silicon—carbon bonds of
various phenylsilanes by hydrogen halides provides a very useful method
for preparing halosilanes of many types (see page 18).[14,123,125,125a,b]

Even in the triorganosilanes, the hydrogen on silicon is more reactive than the hydrogen on carbon in R_3CH compounds. Thus acyl halides react with triorganosilanes to give aldehydes and the corresponding halosilane,[163,164]

$$C_6H_5COCl + (C_6H_5CH_2)_3SiH \longrightarrow C_6H_5CHO + (C_6H_5CH_2)_3SiCl$$

Such a reaction is not known for carbon—hydrogen bonds. In this respect it is worth recalling the reaction between organolithium reagents and the Si—H bond mentioned earlier involving removal of hydride ion, *viz.*

$$R_3SiH + R'Li \longrightarrow R_3SiR' + LiH$$

As an example of the use of this type of reaction in organosilicon synthesis a series of compounds containing the tribenzylsilyl group was recently obtained from tribenzylsilane and the appropriate organolithium reagent.[140] Organolithium compounds do not react with tertiary aliphatic hydrocarbons, and triphenylmethane reacts with R'Li in the reverse manner,

$$(C_6H_5)_3CH + R'Li \longrightarrow (C_6H_5)_3CLi + R'H$$

Grignard reagents react readily with phenyl- and diphenylsilane providing tetrahydrofuran is the solvent to give good yields of the corresponding di- and tri-substituted silanes.[144] This makes it possible to synthesize unsymmetrical organosilicon derivatives containing three or four unlike substituents *via* the reaction sequence,

$$C_6H_5SiH_3 + RMgX \xrightarrow{\text{tetrahydrofuran}} C_6H_5RSiH_2$$

$$C_6H_5RSiH_2 + R'MgX \xrightarrow{\text{tetrahydrofuran}} C_6H_5RR'SiH$$

$$C_6H_5RR'SiH + R''Li \xrightarrow{\text{ether}} C_6H_5RR'R''Si$$

The silicon—hydrogen bond in the organosilanes is susceptible to hydrolysis just as is this bond in the parent silanes. However, as for oxidation and halogenation discussed above, reactivity is much diminished in the organosilanes and decreases along the sequence $RSiH_3$, R_2SiH_2, R_3SiH. Thus the hydrolysis of $RSiH_3$ by alkali is rapid even in a two-phase system, whereas the hydrolysis of R_3SiH by alkali is comparatively slow even in solution. The exact mechanism of the basic hydrolysis of organosilanes, which must involve a nucleophilic attack of hydroxide ion on silicon, has been the subject of much discussion.*   One study in this area has shown[174] that there is a relatively large change in the isotopic rate-ratio for the alkaline hydrolysis of $(C_6H_5)_3SiH$ upon changing from a piperidine-water to an ethanol-water system.   This has led to the conclusion that in the transition state the hydrogen atom of the silane is strongly bonded to a hydrogen atom of the solvent[174]

$$\text{OH}$$
$$\vdots$$
$$[R_3Si \ldots H \ldots H \ldots S]^- \quad \text{(where HS is solvent)}$$

In a mechanism $R_3SiH + OH^- + HS \rightarrow R_3SiOH + H_2 + S^-$ the rate-determining step involves rupture of the Si—H bond.   Because of this, it was suggested that the above reaction path is to be preferred over the alternative mechanism,

$$R_3SiH + OH^- \xrightarrow{\text{slow}} \left[R_3Si \underset{\diagdown H}{\overset{\diagup OH}{}} \right]^- \xrightarrow[\text{fast}]{\text{HS}} R_3SiOH + H_2 + S^-$$

which is also consistent with the viewpoint of a nucleophilic attack on silicon.   Sommer,[283] however, favors the latter mechanism which involves the slow and rate-determining formation of a pentacovalent silicon intermediate.

Hydrogen on silicon in organosilanes is attacked by alcohols in the presence of alkoxide ions just as it is with the parent silanes.   In the case of phenylsilane it has been found possible to control to some extent this alcoholysis reaction so as to obtain alkoxides containing Si—H bonds.[227]   Thus reaction occurs immediately on adding an alcohol dropwise to a rapidly stirred suspension of copper powder in phenylsilane, but the extent of substitution of —OR groups for hydrogen atoms can be limited:

$$C_6H_5SiH_3 + ROH \xrightarrow{\text{Cu}} C_6H_5SiH_2OR + H_2$$

$$C_6H_5SiH_2OR + ROH \xrightarrow{\text{Cu}} C_6H_5SiH(OR)_2 + H_2$$

The lower organosilanes may be thermally decomposed at about 500°.   This has been studied in detail for the ethylsilanes.   Thus at 480° di-

---

* For an authoritative review, see reference 78, page 200 *et seq.*

ethylsilane affords a complex mixture containing C_2H_4, SiH_4, CH_3SiH_3, $(CH_3)_2SiH_2$, C_3H_8, C_3H_6, an oil of composition $C_9H_{24}Si_2$ and polymeric material $(CH_3Si)_x$.[114] This pyrolysis was later modified to increase the amount of material with Si—Si bonds.[121]

As would be expected, because of the presence of silicon—hydrogen bonds, the organosilanes are reducing agents. Triethylsilane reduces certain halides or sulfates of at least ten sub-group elements and five elements in main groups either to a lower oxidation state or sometimes to the free element.[9] Reactions of this type have led to the preparation of certain R_2SiHX and $RSiH_2X$ compounds. Thus gradual addition of a halide of a transitional element ($AgCl$, $HgBr_2$ or $CuCl_2$) to an excess of $(C_2H_5)_2SiH_2$ yields $(C_2H_5)_2SiHCl$ or $(C_2H_5)_2SiHBr$,[9] while a deficiency of $HgCl_2$ or $HgBr_2$ converts n-$C_7H_{15}SiH_3$ into n-$C_7H_{15}SiH_2Cl$ or n-$C_7H_{15}SiH_2Br$.

The ability of organosilanes to reduce halides of certain metals has been developed as a test for the degree of substitution of organo-groups on silicon in the organosilanes.[135] If about one milliliter of a basic solvent, say pyridine, is treated with two drops of a 5% aqueous copper(II) chloride solution and an organosilane is added, an $RSiH_3$ compound discharges the blue color immediately giving a yellow coloration, while an R_2SiH_2 compound discharges the blue color more slowly giving a green coloration, whereas an R_3SiH compound does not discharge the blue color over a three-minute period.

Certain ketones may be reduced by heating them strongly with diphenylsilane,[72]

$$(C_6H_5)_2CO \xrightarrow[260°]{(C_6H_5)_2SiH_2} (C_6H_5)_2CH_2$$

Similarly, as mentioned above, tribenzylsilane will convert benzoyl chloride to benzaldehyde.[164] These reduction reactions are similar to those found with phenyltin hydrides (Chap. 4, Sec. B) but require much higher temperatures.

Diphenylsilane undergoes a remarkable reaction when heated with sulfur-containing heterocycles.[343] Hydrogen sulfide is slowly evolved, and compounds are formed, albeit in poor yield, in which the sulfur atom is replaced by the diphenylsilylene group, viz.,

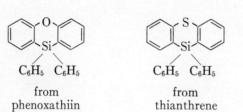 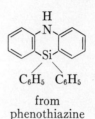

from	from	from
phenoxathiin	thianthrene	phenothiazine

On the other hand, reduction of a carbonyl group rather than replacement of a sulfur atom occurs in the reaction,[72]

Phenylsilanes disproportionate very easily in the presence of aluminum chloride in benzene but not in ether solution.[141,285]

$$4C_6H_5SiH_3 \longrightarrow (C_6H_5)_4Si + 3SiH_4$$

$$4C_6H_5(CH_3)SiH_2 \longrightarrow (C_6H_5)_4Si + 2CH_3SiH_3 + (CH_3)_2SiH_2$$

The silane formed in some of these reactions can cause explosions and phenylsilicon hydrides should not be brought into contact with strong Lewis acids unless appropriate precautions are taken.

Mention has already been made in this section of compounds wherein alkyl groups, halogen atoms and hydrogen atoms are all bonded to the same silicon atom. These compounds disproportionate readily in the presence of aluminum chloride in reactions reminiscent of the SiH—SiCl interchanges mentioned earlier:

$$2(C_2H_5)_2SiHCl \xrightarrow{AlCl_3} (C_2H_5)_2SiCl_2 + (C_2H_5)_2SiH_2 \qquad (36)$$

Methylhalosilanes have proved to be useful intermediates for the synthesis of many substances, the properties of which have added to our knowledge of the nature of bonds to silicon.

$$2CH_3SiH_2I + H_2O \longrightarrow (CH_3SiH_2)_2O + 2HI \qquad (94)$$

$$2CH_3SiH_2I + HgS \longrightarrow (CH_3SiH_2)_2S + HgI_2 \qquad (94)$$

$$2(CH_3)_2SiHI + Ag_2CO_3 \longrightarrow [(CH_3)_2SiH]_2O + 2AgI + CO_2 \qquad (97)$$

$$2(CH_3)_2SiHI + HgS \longrightarrow [(CH_3)_2SiH]_2S + HgI_2 \tag{97}$$

$$3CH_3SiH_2Cl + 4NH_3 \longrightarrow (CH_3SiH_2)_3N + 3NH_4Cl \tag{80}$$

$$2CH_3SiH_2Cl + 3CH_3NH_2 \longrightarrow (CH_3SiH_2)_2NCH_3 + 2CH_3NH_3Cl \tag{80}$$

$$CH_3SiH_2I + 2(CH_3)_2NH \longrightarrow (CH_3SiH_2)N(CH_3)_2 + (CH_3)_2NH_2I \tag{80}$$

$$CH_3SiH_2I + AgCN \longrightarrow CH_3SiH_2NC^* + AgI \tag{94}$$

$$(CH_3)_2SiHI + AgCN \longrightarrow (CH_3)_2SiHNC^* + AgI \tag{191}$$

$$CH_3SiH_2I + AgCNS \longrightarrow CH_3SiH_2NCS + AgI \tag{191}$$

Reactions listed here should serve to remind the reader of analogous reactions involving SiH_3X compounds which yield $(SiH_3)_2O$, $(SiH_3)_2NCH_3$ and the like.   Indeed, one of the objects of making some of these methyl-silyl derivatives was to compare their Lewis basicity with that of the unsubstituted silyl compounds.   On the basis of the electron-releas-ing properties of the methyl group, it would be anticipated that $(CH_3SiH_2)_2S$ would be a stronger electron pair donor than $(SiH_3)_2S$, and $(CH_3SiH_2)_2NCH_3$ a stronger electron pair donor than $(SiH_3)_2NCH_3$. Unfortunately, no acceptor molecule has been found which can clearly demonstrate differences in basicity among these various compounds.   For example, both $(CH_3SiH_2)_2S$[93] and $(CH_3SiH_2)_2NCH_3$[80] form no adduct with trimethylboron, being quite similar in this respect to $CH_3N(SiH_3)_2$.[306] There has been no report of an attempt to make $(SiH_3)_2S \cdot B(CH_3)_3$, but it is most unlikely that such a compound would exist.[200]   The compound $(CH_3)_2S \cdot B(CH_3)_3$, however, does form at low temperatures,[147] and since it is most improbable that lattice energies would be a determining factor in compounds of this type, the existence of dimethyl sulfide-trimethyl-boron and the non-existence of trimethylboron adducts of disilyl sulfide and 1,1′-dimethyldisilthiane[95] is most unexpected in terms of simple atomic electronegativity values.   The suggestion[15,48,89,300] that a cer-tain amount of d_π—p_π bonding is present in the silicon compounds is, however, consistent with the experimental facts.[89,93,97,191,306]

When the methylsilyl derivatives of oxygen[93] and nitrogen[80] are treated with boron trifluoride and boron trichloride, adducts are formed at low temperatures, but these decompose rapidly in an irreversible man-ner, thereby making it impossible to use boron halides as reference acids

---

* Although these compounds have been formulated by the discoverers as *iso*-cyanides, they may well be cyanides, or mixtures of cyanides and *iso*cyanides.[30,103]

for determining the relative base strengths of the silicon compounds. The decomposition reactions involve a shift of fluoride or chloride on boron to silicon, e.g.,[80,93]

$$(CH_3SiH_2)_2O + BX_3 \longrightarrow CH_3SiH_2OBX_2 + CH_3SiH_2X$$

$$3CH_3SiH_2OBX_2 \longrightarrow 3CH_3SiH_2X + BX_3 + B_2O_3$$

$$(CH_3SiH_2)_3N + BF_3 \longrightarrow (CH_3SiH_2)_3N \cdot BF_3 \longrightarrow CH_3SiH_2F$$
$$+ (CH_3SiH_2)_2NBF_2$$

It is interesting that fluoride shift reactions are common in boron trifluoride chemistry. Thus BF_3 reacts with $(CH_3BO)_3$[46] to yield CH_3BF_2, and with $(CH_3)_2BN(CH_3)_2$[47] to yield $(CH_3)_2BF$, and mention has already been made in this volume of the reaction of $(SiH_3)_3N$ with BF_3 to yield SiH_3F and $(SiH_3)_2NBF_2$,[307] and of SiH_3OCH_3 with BF_3 to yield SiH_3F and CH_3OBF_2.[290a]

It is appropriate to mention here that strong Lewis acids also cleave the silicon—oxygen bond in hexamethyldisiloxane. Thus, treatment of the latter with BF_3 at $-96°$ yields a solid 1:1 adduct, but on warming to $-78°$ some $(CH_3)_3SiF$ is produced, although most of the combined boron trifluoride is recovered.[93] The stronger Lewis acids aluminum chloride and bromide readily react with hexamethyldisiloxane[58]

$$[(CH_3)_3Si]_2O + AlX_3 \longrightarrow (CH_3)_3SiX + (CH_3)_3SiOAlX_2$$

The trimethylsiloxyaluminum dihalides are much more stable than their boron analogues. Hexamethyldisiloxane, like disiloxane, has no clearly recognizable donor properties. Full substitution of hydrogen on silicon in $(SiH_3)_2O$ by methyl groups fails to counteract the effects of silicon-oxygen $d_\pi—p_\pi$ bonding. In this respect the behavior of iodine in $[(CH_3)_3Si]_2O$ is most interesting.[58] The color is a purple very similar to that of iodine in carbon tetrachloride. In donor solvents such as alcohols, ethers and olefins, iodine gives a brown color as a result of complex formation.

In concluding discussion of the methylsilyl compounds of oxygen, sulfur and nitrogen, it may be mentioned that these substances react with hydrogen halides, and are hydrolyzed in a manner similar to the unsubstituted compounds like $(SiH_3)_2S$ or $(SiH_3)_3N$.

$$(CH_3SiH_2)_2S + H_2O \longrightarrow 2(CH_3SiH_2)_2O + H_2S \tag{94}$$

$$(CH_3SiH_2)_3N + 4HCl \longrightarrow 3CH_3SiH_2Cl + NH_4Cl \tag{80}$$

D. Some Physicochemical Studies Made on Compounds Containing Si—H Bonds

1. THERMOCHEMICAL STUDIES

Values reported for the heat of formation of monosilane have varied from -8.7 kcal. mole^{-1} to -14.8 kcal. mole^{-1}. A much more reliable value of $+7.8 \pm 3.5$ kcal. mole^{-1} has been obtained from a study of the decomposition of SiH_4 at 680° into crystalline silicon and hydrogen.[39] A recent study[149] of the heat of explosive combustion of a mixture of silane and stibine has led to a value of 7.3 ± 0.3 kcal. mole^{-1} for $\Delta H_f^\circ(SiH_4)$, in good agreement with the result obtained by decomposing silane at 680°. The positive value for the heat of formation of silane is in better accord with the properties of the hydride than are the negative values of heat of formation obtained previously. Furthermore, it is evident that the stability of silane at ambient temperatures is due to a slow rate of decomposition rather than to any favorable equilibrium constant. The measured[149] heat of formation of silane implies a Si—H bond energy in the hydride of 76.5 kcal.

The activation energy for pyrolysis of disilane has been determined as 51.3 kcal.[91] In later work a value of 48.9 kcal. was obtained.[295] The activation energy for the thermal decomposition of silane is similar to that for disilane.[159] It has been suggested[91,95] that the activation energy for pyrolysis of disilane may be taken as the silicon—silicon bond energy. However, the mechanism for the decomposition of Si_2H_6 has not been completely elucidated,[295] and, moreover, even if the initial reaction step is $Si_2H_6 \rightarrow SiH_3 + SiH_3$, as suggested in the original work,[95] the activation energy of the reverse or recombination reaction may not be zero. Only if this assumption is true does the bond dissociation energy equal the activation energy.[56] It has been mentioned previously (page 16) that when the decomposition of Si_2H_6 is carried out in the presence of hydrogen the yield of SiH_4 is increased, and that this fact supported the contention[95] that SiH_3 radicals were involved in the decomposition of disilane.*

---

* Silyl radicals are undoubtedly involved in some of the chemistry of the hydrides Si_nH_{2n+2}, e.g., during the addition of Si—H bonds to carbon—carbon double bonds under certain reaction conditions. Indeed, SiH_3 radicals have been formed at 4° Abs. in an argon matrix and their electron spin resonance spectrum studied.[55]

However, it should be noted[295] that if the primary step in the decomposition of disilane is an alternative one like $Si_2H_6 \rightarrow SiH_4 + SiH_2$, the amount of silane formed would also be increased by addition of hydrogen. Nevertheless, in spite of these complicating factors, a recent determination of the heat of formation of disilane has led to a Si—Si thermochemical bond energy of 46.4 kcal.,[149] a result fairly close to the value (48.9 kcal) suggested by the pyrolysis study.[295]

The silicon—carbon bond energies in some alkylsilanes have been calculated[311] from the heats of combustion of the compounds.[312] It has been found that in the methylsilanes the Si—C bond energy is about 74 kcal., in the ethylsilanes between about 60 and 65 kcal., and in the butylsilanes about 56 kcal. These values appear to indicate a definite dependence of Si—C bond energy on the nature of the alkyl group bonded to silicon. However, the discrepancies may be due to a breakdown of the assumption of strict additivity of bond energies in organo-silicon compounds, or to the difficulty in obtaining reliable heats of formation of these compounds.

2. DIFFRACTION STUDIES

Several electron diffraction studies have been made on compounds containing silicon—hydrogen bonds. As far as the electron diffraction technique is concerned, some of these studies are relatively old, while others are comparatively recent. Only in the latter case have interatomic distances and bond angles been obtained with an accuracy comparable to that made possible by using spectroscopic techniques (see below).

Examples of early work are studies on Si_2H_6 (Si—Si bond distance 2.32 ± 0.03 Å, Si—H bond distance 1.47 ± 0.03 Å),[42] $SiHCl_3$,[42,155] SiH_2Cl_2,[43] SiH_3Cl[43] and $SiHBr_3$.[287,346] More recently electron diffraction investigations have demonstrated the planarity of the Si_3N skeleton in $(SiH_3)_3N$ (Si—N bond distance 1.738 ± 0.020 Å, <Si—N—Si = 119.6° to within 1.0°),[154] and the large <Si—O—Si (141°) in $(SiH_3)_2O$.[105] The implications of the structure of these silyl compounds to the concept of π-bonding in certain silicon compounds have been discussed in previous sections of this volume.

The sector-microphotometer method has been used in an electron diffraction study of mono-, di-, and trimethylsilane.[31] The results suggest an apparent smooth increase in Si—C distance from 1.857 ± 0.007 Å in CH_3SiH_3, 1.860 ± 0.004 Å in $(CH_3)_2SiH_2$, to 1.873 ± 0.006 Å in

$(CH_3)_3SiH.$* The Si—H bond distance was found to be 1.48 ± 0.02 Å in fair agreement with values obtained with other molecules and using other techniques. It is interesting to note that the Si—C distances in all the methylsilanes are significantly less than would be expected in terms of bond additivities. The average of the Si—Si distance in Si_2Cl_6 and Si_2H_6 is 2.30 Å. This implies a Si—C distance of 1.92 Å taking the covalent radius of carbon as 0.77 Å.† It is just possible that this apparent bond shortening is due to a partial release of electron density from the methyl groups to the silicon, so that the Si—C bonding in the methylsilanes might be similar to that proposed for B—C bonding in trimethylboron.[231] In the case of boron the acceptor orbital is a p_π, whereas in silicon the acceptor orbitals would be d_π. However, it must be recognized that arguments based on the summation of bond radii assume the validity of this concept, and it has been suggested by some[69] that there is in fact little justification for the rule of additivity of covalent radii. Although this viewpoint would appear to represent an extreme, it certainly serves to emphasize that additivity arguments should be applied with great care. For example, an electron diffraction study[178] has led to a value for the Si—C distance in $C_6H_5SiH_3$ of 1.84 ± 0.01 Å. This leads to a 0.017 Å contraction‡ of the Si—C distance compared with that in CH_3SiH_3 using the electron diffraction data.[31] One might tend to use this fact to support an argument that in phenylsilane there is d_π—p_π bonding using the phenyl group's π-electrons and the vacant silicon d-orbitals. However, the carbon radii in $C_6H_5SiH_3$ (sp^2 carbon) will be less than the carbon radius in CH_3SiH_3 (sp^3 carbon), and this difference

---

* Application of the electron diffraction technique to tetramethylsilane has led to a value of 1.888 ± 0.020 Å for the Si—C distance, see reference 276.

† The Schomaker-Stevenson equation[270] which corrects for the polar character of covalent bonds predicts an Si—C distance of 1.88 Å in fair agreement with the observed values from the electron diffraction study and in good agreement with the microwave results (Table 6). However, the Schomaker-Stevenson equation is empirical and has been criticized.[331] In particular, in silicon chemistry it predicts Si—F distances significantly larger than observed.

‡ If the microwave results for CH_3SiH_3 (Table 6) are taken the calculated contraction is 0.027Å. It is also interesting to note that in passing from methylsilane (sp^3 carbon) to vinylsilane (sp^2 carbon) microwave results indicate an Si—C bond shortening of only 0.014Å. This is discussed in reference 239.

in carbon radii is probably quite sufficient to explain the bond shortening in passing from the aliphatic to the aromatic compound. It should not be thought from this, though, that when a silicon atom is bonded to a phenyl or vinyl group there is no d_π—p_π bonding supplementing the σ-bond. As discussed elsewhere,[52,78,300] there is evidence that conjugation of a silicon atom with an aromatic or vinyl system does occur, but it is not yet clear what effect if any π-bonding involving silicon $3d$-orbitals would have on Si—C distances. All that is implied here is that the concept of strict additivity of bond radii is in such a dubious state that arguments concerning the degree of bond multiplicity based on bond distances can be misleading.

3. SPECTROSCOPIC STUDIES

The infrared spectrum of silane under high resolution has been studied by several groups of workers.[37,254,291,316] Early work confirmed the tetrahedral structure of silane and led to a value of 1.456 Å for the Si—H distance.[316] This bond distance is subject to some error because its determination required the rotational analysis of two infrared-active fundamentals in SiH_4 which are complicated by the existence of strong Coriolis perturbations. Because of this difficulty later workers studied the spectra of SiH_3D[254] and SiD_3H,[37] obtaining values for the Si—H distance in silane of 1.477 ± 0.003 Å and 1.4798 ± 0.0004 Å, respectively, on the assumption that this parameter remains unchanged by isotopic substitution. Subsequently, the infrared spectra of a variety of deuterated silanes were observed and the band assignments and force constants calculated.[225]

A thorough study of the Raman spectrum of liquid and the infrared spectrum of gaseous Si_2H_6 has been made.[29] This followed some earlier studies of the Raman spectrum[292] and the infrared spectrum.[150] Of particular interest is the question as to whether disilane has hindered internal rotation as does ethane. The results[29,150] show that the molecule is indeed a hindered internal rotator, and it has been suggested[150] that the potential barrier to internal rotation is about one kilocalorie. It is very interesting that internal rotation is still hindered in disilane in view of the fact that the Si—Si distance is appreciably greater than the C—C distance in ethane.

TABLE 6. MICROWAVE STUDIES ON DERIVATIVES OF SILANE.

Compound	Barrier Height Hindering Internal Rotation about Si–C bond (cal/mole)	Structural Parameters				Reference
CH_3SiH_3	1700	SiC	1.8668 ± 0.0005 Å	<HCH	107°40' ± 30'	181
		CH	1.093 ± 0.005 Å	<HSiH	108°15' ± 30'	
		SiH	1.485 ± 0.005 Å			
$(CH_3)_2SiH_2$	1647	SiH	1.483 ± 0.005 Å	<CSiC	110°59' ± 10'	250
		CH	1.095 ± 0.005 Å	<HSiH	107°50' ± 20'	
		SiC	1.867 ± 0.002 Å	<HCH	108°0' ± 20'	
$(CH_3)_3SiH$	~1830	CH	1.095 ± 0.002 Å	<CSiC	110°10' ± 12'	251
		SiH	1.489 ± 0.001 Å	<HCH	107°56' ± 14'	
		SiC	1.868 ± 0.002 Å			
$CH_2:CHSiH_3$	1500	C=C	1.347 ± 0.003 Å	<SiC=C	122°53' ± 15'	239
		SiH	1.475 ± 0.005 Å	<HSiH	108°42' ± 20'	
		CH(cis)	1.097 ± 0.005 Å	<C=CH (cis)	120°18' ± 20'	
		CH	1.094 ± 0.005 Å	<C=CH (trans)	120°38' ± 20'	
		SiC	1.853 ± 0.003 Å	<C=CH	117°59' ± 20'	
CH_3SiHF_2	1255	SiC	1.833 ± 0.002 Å	<FSiF	106°44' ± 30'	308
		SiF	1.583 ± 0.002 Å	<HSiC	116°10' ± 1'	
		SiH	1.474 ± 0.005 Å	<FSiC	109°52' ± 30'	

Compound		Bond	Distance	Angle		Ref.
CH₃SiH₂F	1559	SiC	1.848 ± 0.005 Å	<CSiF	109°13' ± 30'	249
		SiF	1.600 ± 0.005 Å	<HCH	107°52' ± 30'	
		SiH	1.473 ± 0.005 Å			
		CH	1.090 ± 0.005 Å			
SiH₃F		SiH	1.470 to 1.452 Å	<FSiH	109°26' to 110°	18
		SiF	1.595 ± 0.010 Å			
SiH₂F₂		SiH	1.471 ± 0.007 Å	<HSiH	112°1' ± 30'	196
		SiF	1.5767 ± 0.001 Å	<FSiF	107°56' ± 6'	
SiHF₃		SiH	1.455 ± 0.01 Å	<FSiF	108°17' ± 30'	153,277
		SiF	1.565 ± 0.005 Å			
SiH₃Cl		SiCl	2.0479 ± 0.0007 Å	<ClSiH	109°40' to 109°20'	17,18
		SiH	1.483 ± 0.010 Å			
		SiH	1.481 ± 0.001 Å			180
SiH₃Br		SiBr	2.209 ± 0.001 Å	<HSiH	111°20' ± 1°	275
		SiH	1.57 ± 0.03 Å			
		SiH	1.483 ± 0.001 Å			180
SiH₃I		SiH	1.488 ± 0.001 Å			180
SiH₃CN		SiC	1.848 Å			278
		CN	1.156 Å			229a
SiH₃NCS		SiH	1.48 ± 0.01 Å	<HSiN	108°30' ± 1°	161
		SiS	4.485 ± 0.003 Å			
		SiN	1.729 ± 0.020 Å			
		NC	1.196 ± 0.020 Å			

Infrared and Raman spectra of the halosilanes, particularly the silyl halides, SiH_3X, have been the subject of several investigations, e.g. SiH_3F,[234] SiH_3Cl,[234] SiH_3Br,[219,234] SiH_3I,[74] SiD_3I,[207] SiH_2Cl_2,[151] SiH_2Br_2,[219] $SiHCl_3$,[151] and $SiHF_3$.[235] From some of these studies, as well as from microwave work described below, it is certain that these halides all have a tetrahedral structure. One of the investigations of infrared spectra[234] is of particular importance when combined with microwave data, since it has enabled the silicon-hydrogen distance to be computed with better accuracy than is attainable when microwave data alone is used. In the microwave work the Si—H distance is strongly affected by small errors in the microwave frequencies or by mass differences between the isotopic atoms. It is also interesting that in the SiH_3X compounds[234] the dimensions of the SiH_3 group vary but little from molecule to molecule, and that the value of the Si—H distance (1.476 Å in SiH_3Cl) is very close to the values in SiH_3D[254] and SiD_3H[37] (see above).

Accumulation of structural and spectral data has permitted calculation of heat content, free energy, entropy and heat capacity of SiH_4,[2,50] SiH_3Cl,[50] SiH_3Br and SiH_2Br_2.[219]

A number of studies of infrared and Raman spectra have been made on compounds wherein a silyl group is bonded to nitrogen, phosphorus, oxygen, sulfur or carbon.

The infrared spectra of $(SiH_3)_3N$ and $(SiD_3)_3N$ in the gas phase, and the Raman spectrum of liquid $(SiH_3)_3N$ have been obtained.[81] The combined results provide evidence for a planar Si_3N structure, thereby confirming the earlier results of electron diffraction.[154] A stretching force constant of 4.0×10^5 dyn. cm^{-1} was calculated for the Si—N bond in $(SiH_3)_3N$. It has been suggested that since this stretching force constant is within what is usually regarded as the single-bond range, the amount of π-bonding in trisilylamine is not very large. However, in inorganic chemistry, it is not necessarily correct to correlate bond multiplicity with force constants. There is no theoretical reason why some σ, π-bonds involving d-orbitals should not be weaker than many single bonds.

The infrared and Raman spectra of the molecules $N_2(SiH_3)_4$ and $N_2(SiD_3)_4$ have been recorded.[16] The planarity of the nitrogen and silicon atoms in trisilylamine suggests that in tetrasilylhydrazine the heavy atoms will be arranged in an ethylene-like manner (point group D_{2h}) or in a corresponding configuration in which one end has been turned through 90° as in gaseous B_2Cl_4 (point group D_{2d}). Although, because of experimental difficulties, the spectra of tetrasilylhydrazine were incomplete, the results strongly favor a D_{2d} structure. This of course is in contrast to the structure of tetramethylhydrazine (point group C_2), and reflects the presence of N—Si π-bonding in the silicon compound.

An examination[265a] of the infrared spectrum of N,N',N''-trisilylcyclo-trisilazane showed the presence of absorptions due to SiH_3 groups[81] and SiH_2 groups,[182] in accordance with the heterocyclic $(SiH_3NSiH_2)_3$ structure proposed.[265a]

The infrared spectrum of silylphosphine (SiH_3PH_2) has been recorded, and discussed in comparison with the spectrum of methylphosphine.[208]

Brief mention has been made previously of studies on the vibrational spectrum of disiloxane. This molecule has taken considerable punishment from the spectroscopists, presumably stimulated by the reported unusual chemical properties[48] and structure[154] of trisilylamine, and by the dearth of simple inorganic molecules which have not as yet been examined by the infrared and Raman techniques. The first exhaustive investigation of the vibrational spectra of $(SiH_3)_2O$ and $(SiD_3)_2O$ revealed an obvious lack of coincidences between infrared and Raman frequencies, and from this it was concluded that the molecule had a linear skeleton.[210] However, a study of the infrared spectrum of disiloxane in argon and nitrogen matrices[59] strongly suggests that the silyl derivative is bent, as does a study[221] of the spectrum of the molecule at liquid air temperatures. Nevertheless, as has been pointed out elsewhere,[221] it is not necessary that disiloxane should have the same structure in the solid and gaseous states. Of greater significance is a different approach[221] whereby a potential function is calculated for disiloxane, assuming the stretching interaction force constant involving two Si—X bonds is the same in the amine and in the ether. Such a calculation leads to an Si—O—Si angle of between 140° and 150°. This is in good agreement with the electron diffraction study mentioned previously.[105] A Raman spectrum study of a 1:1 mixture of $(SiH_3)_2{}^{18}O$ and $(SiH_3)_2{}^{16}O$ also provides strong evidence that the Si—O—Si angle is less than 180°.[222]

As a result of all this work the reader should not lose sight of its most important consequence, namely, that the Si—O—Si angle, be it 180° or, as now seems more likely, about 150°, is far larger than the C—O—C angle in $(CH_3)_2O$ and that this strongly supports the idea of d_π—p_π bonding in disiloxane.[89,300]

As mentioned in an earlier section, the infrared and Raman spectra of $(SiH_3)_2S$[84,204] and $(SiH_3)_2Se$[84] clearly indicate that the Si—X—Si skeletons are non-linear, and that the spectrum of "SiH_3CN" is better interpreted by assuming a cyanide rather than an *iso*cyanide structure for this compound. Satisfactory vibrational assignments for the infrared spectrum of SiH_3SCF_3 have been made.[75]

The infrared and Raman spectra of disilylacetylene have been studied, and these spectra confirm the expected linearity of the molecule and show that the compound is a free internal rotator.[209]

A comprehensive study has been made of the infrared spectra of the compounds $(CH_3SiH_2)_nX$ where X = CH_3, F, Cl, Br and I when $n = 1$; where X = O or S when $n = 2$; and where X = N when $n = 3$.[82] Assignment of frequencies has been made for the vibrations of the SiH_2 group and for the Si—X bond stretching modes.

The infrared spectra of a number of organosilanes have been recorded, and these spectra are very useful for identification purposes.[177,280,333] A study[19] of the infrared and Raman spectra of dimethyl- and trimethylsilanes has led to an almost complete band assignment. The frequencies associated with the silicon-hydrogen vibrational modes in a large number of organosilanes have been the subject of comprehensive study.[182,281] It is possible to correlate the silicon-hydrogen frequency with the nature of the other groups bonded to silicon. Thus in compounds of the type $R_1R_2R_3Si$—H the vibration frequency of the Si—H bond is given approximately by the relation:

$$\nu(Si—H) = 2106 + 17.5\Sigma\sigma^*$$

where σ^* is the Taft inductive factor of the attached groups.[315] Such a relationship assumes that the Si—H vibration frequency is controlled by inductive effects and mesomeric influences play little part. This assumption is reasonable so long as the substituents R on silicon do not possess π-electrons able to partake in π-bonding with the vacant $3d$-orbitals of silicon.

The proton nuclear magnetic resonance spectra of a number of compounds containing silicon—hydrogen bonds have been examined. One investigation of interest in this field involved the series of compounds $(SiH_3)_3N$, $CH_3N(SiH_3)_2$, $(CH_3)_2NSiH_3$ and $(CH_3)_3N$.[83] Chemical shift values of the methyl-proton resonances change appreciably in the series of molecules, but the silyl-proton resonances remain fairly constant. The relative shifts are such that the protons bound to carbon become less shielded as the methyl groups are replaced by silyls, i.e., the nitrogen atom withdraws electrons more strongly. This is in keeping with the relative base strength studies of the silylamines discussed earlier.

The nuclear magnetic resonance spectra of alkyl- and aryl-trisubstituted silanes have been studied, and the positions of the absorptions due to the proton attached directly to silicon have been measured.[330] The chemical shift for the proton in trichlorosilane was also recorded. In general the shielding values decreased with increasing electronegativity of the substituent group: with trichlorosilane, as expected, being at one end of the series, the chloro-substituent being the most electronegative studied. It has also been possible to correlate chemical shift with the inductive effect in the series $(CH_3)_xCl_{3-x}SiH$ and $(CH_3)_xCl_{3-x}CH$ ($x = 0$ to 3). Successive replacement of methyl groups by the more electronegative chlorine results in a progressive decrease in the shielding of the proton bound to the silicon or to the central carbon atom. A similar effect is found for the methylphenylsilanes and the analogous carbon series, replacement of methyl groups by the more electronegative phenyl groups leading to a progressive decrease in the shielding value for the proton resonances. In the series $(CH_3)_xCl_{3-x}SiH$ and $(CH_3)_xCl_{3-x}CH$, and again in the series $(CH_3)_x(C_6H_5)_{3-x}SiH$ and $(CH_3)_x(C_6H_5)_{3-x}CH$, as chlorine is substituted for methyl or phenyl is substituted for methyl the change in (C—)H chemical shifts is much larger than the change in (Si—)H chemical shifts. It is possible that this effect is due to p_π—d_π bonding in the silicon compounds between π-electrons of chlorine atoms or phenyl groups and the silicon $3d$ orbitals. If this occurred it would be expected to reduce the effect of change of substituent in the silicon series by virtue of a tendency to increase electron density on the silicon atoms. In the carbon series with no π-bonding likely an inductive effect would not be opposed by a mesomeric effect. Whatever are the factors which determine (Si—)H shieldings, and as with (C—)H proton shieldings they may be many, it is interesting that these same factors appear to govern Si—H stretching vibration frequencies since, except when phenyl and possibly vinyl groups are bound to silicon, a straight line plot between $\nu_{Si-H}(cm^{-1})$ and τ(p.p.m.) is obtained.[330]

The ^{1}H and [19]F n.m.r. spectra of silane derivatives SiH_nX_{4-n} (X = halogen) have been studied to determine variations in H—H and H—[29]Si coupling constants.* In contrast to the corresponding carbon compounds the magnitude of J_{HH} was found to increase with increasing H—Si—H angle. A linear relationship between J_{HH} and J_{SiH} was also observed.[85]

Microwave spectra of several organosilanes and halosilanes have been studied in order to determine the structural parameters of the molecules and in addition, in the case of the organosilanes, to measure the potential barriers hindering internal rotation of methyl groups about the Si—C bonds. Methylsilane and its substituted derivatives are the analogues of ethane and the substituted ethanes which have also been studied by the microwave technique. In these studies of special interest has been the potential barriers hindering internal rotation about the C—C bonds. For a general discussion of this subject the reader is referred to reference 340.

Silicon compounds containing Si—H bonds investigated by the microwave technique are listed in Table 6, and several interesting conclusions can be drawn. According to the microwave data, and in contrast to the electron diffraction results, methylation of methylsilane has no detectable effect on the Si—C distance. As pointed out elsewhere,[251] this discrepancy is not serious since the electron diffraction study gave results with an uncertainty of ± 0.006 Å, whereas the experimental uncertainty (± 0.002 Å) in the microwave study is less. In passing from methylsilane to methyldifluorosilane the Si—C bond length decreases.[190,251] This may perhaps be due to resonance structures such as

* The isotope [29]Si has a nuclear spin of $\frac{1}{2}$, and has a 5 per cent abundance in naturally occurring silicon. Coupling constants [29]Si-H are, therefore, easily obtained.

becoming more important with increasing substitution of hydrogen by the electronegative fluorine, a procedure likely to lower the energy of the silicon $3d$ orbitals making them more available for bonding. It should also be noted that the Si—F distance in the fluorosilanes is less than expected. The Schomaker-Stevenson rule predicts an Si—F distance of 169. Å. Assuming the validity of the concept of additivity of bond radii the observed values can be rationalized in terms of fluorine-silicon p_π—d_π bonding.

H

GERMANIUM

THE GERMANIUM HYDRIDES

AND RELATED COMPOUNDS

At this time much less is known of the chemistry of the germanes than of the silanes. Indeed, until very recently only *three* volatile binary germanium-hydrogen compounds had been unambiguously identified. These were germane (GeH_4), digermane (Ge_2H_6), and trigermane (Ge_3H_8). However, some recent work on the hydrolysis of magnesium germanide and the effect of an electrical discharge on GeH_4 has shown that several higher germanes are capable of existence. A number of hitherto unknown halogen derivatives of monogermane have also recently been characterized. In addition to these volatile germanes solid non-volatile materials containing only germanium and hydrogen have long been known.

Other well-characterized compounds containing germanium and hydrogen include halogen derivatives of monogermane, and some organogermanes, $R_n GeH_{4-n}$ (n = 1, 2 or 3) (Table 7).

TABLE 7. THE GERMANES AND SOME RELATED COMPOUNDS.*

Compound	M.P.	B.P.	Reference	Compound	M.P.	B.P.	Reference
GeH_4	$-166°$	$-88.4°$	54	CH_3GeH_3	$-158°$	$-35.1°$	6
Ge_2H_6	$-109°$	$29°$	86	CH_3GeH_2Cl	$-101°$	$70.9°$	6
Ge_3H_8	$-105.6°$	$110.5°$	65,86	CH_3GeHCl_2	$-62.1°$	$113.2°$	6
GeH_3F	$-22°$	$15.6°$	289	$C_2H_5GeH_3$	$\dots$	$9.2°$	313
GeH_3Cl	$-52°$	$28°$	66	$n\text{-}C_3H_7GeH_3$	$\dots$	$30°$	168
GeH_2Cl_2	$-68°$	$69.5°$	66	$(CH_3)_2GeH_2$	$-149°$	$-0.6°$	6
$GeHCl_3$	$-71°$	$75°$	$\dots$†	$(CH_3)_2GeHCl$	$-76°$	$89.4°$	6
GeH_3Br	$-32°$	$52°$	66	$(C_2H_5)_3GeH$	$\dots$	$124.4°/751mm$	165,184
GeH_2Br_2	$-15°$	$89°$	66	$(C_6H_5)_3GeH$	$47° (\alpha)$ $27° (\beta)$	$\dots$	166
GeH_3I	$-15°$	$0°/20$ mm	303				
GeH_2I_2	$-44.9°$	$0° < 0.1$ mm	303	$CH_2{:}CHGeH_3$	$\dots$	$-3.5°$	40

* For a more detailed listing of compounds having Ge—H bonds the reader is referred to Gmelins Handbuch der Anorganischen Chemie, Germanium (1958).

† From patent literature, see reference mentioned in previous footnote.

A. Preparation of the Germanes

All the methods described earlier for obtaining silicon—hydrogen bonds can be used for creating germanium—hydrogen bonds. In addition, because of the relatively high stability of the Ge—H bond in aqueous solution (monogermane is but little decomposed by 40% alkali), it is possible to prepare germane and some of its organo-derivatives by routes not applicable to the preparation of silane and the organosilanes. It is interesting that one of these routes, reduction of germanium tetrachloride with zinc and sulfuric acid, was the first used to obtain germane, although the compound was not obtained in quantity sufficient for accurate identification.[325] Later workers prepared germane in amounts sufficient for identification by reducing solutions of germanium in sulfuric acid with zinc or magnesium,[242] and by treating a magnesium-germanium alloy with acid.[268] The latter method for preparing germane is analogous to that used by Stock and his co-workers to obtain the boranes and the silanes.[293] Because of Stock's success in obtaining these hydrides from magnesium boride and magnesium silicide, Dennis, Corey and Moore[65] were prompted to hydrolyze magnesium germanide with dilute hydrochloric acid, and they thereby obtained in about 27% yield a mixture of GeH_4, Ge_2H_6 and Ge_3H_8. This work must be regarded as the classic investigation in germanium hydride chemistry since it resulted not only in characterization of the three hydrides, and indications of the existence of still higher hydrides, but also in a preliminary study of the chemical properties of the compounds. Subsequently, mixtures of germanes (yield about 70%), in which monogermane predominated, were obtained from the reaction between ammonium bromide and magnesium germanide in liquid ammonia.[183] Recently the mixture of gases obtained by the acid hydrolysis of magnesium germanide has been subjected to chromatography.[35] Seven peaks were observed, the first five probably being due to the hydrides GeH_4, Ge_2H_6, Ge_3H_8, $iso\text{-}Ge_4H_{10}$, and $n\text{-}Ge_4H_{10}$. Another recent study[3] of the hydrolysis of magnesium germanide has led to the isolation of two hydrides Ge_4H_{10} (B.P. 176.9° extrap.) and Ge_5H_{12} (B.P. 234° extrap.), but in view of the chromatography work mentioned above and the electric discharge work mentioned below, it is not clear to which isomers the formulae refer, or whether the products are in fact mixtures of isomers. The hydride "Ge_4H_{10}" decomposes slowly above 50° and rapidly above 100° to afford germane and a higher liquid germane. The oily liquid "Ge_5H_{12}" at 100° yields germane and a solid. Above 350° both Ge_4H_{10} and Ge_5H_{12} decompose to germanium and hydrogen.

A useful electric-discharge procedure has recently been found to afford higher germanes.[76a] Circulation of monogermane through a silent electric discharge at a pressure of about 0.5 atm. yields a mixture of Ge_2H_6 and Ge_3H_8 which was separated by vacuum distillation, and a mixture of other species including hepta- and octa-germanes which was separated by vapor phase chromatography. The various hydrides, including isomers, were identified by chromatographic retention times, proton magnetic resonance spectra and mass spectrometry. Typical yields in terms of germanium in monogermane consumed were: digermane 20%, trigermane 30%, tetragermanes 6%, pentagermanes 0.4%, hexagermanes 0.12%, heptagermanes 0.1%, and octagermanes 0.04%.

Since the discovery of lithium aluminum hydride and other complex metal hydrides, the above reactions as routes for obtaining *monogermane* are only of classical interest.

In early work with lithium aluminum hydride $GeCl_4$ was reduced to GeH_4[111] in a manner similar to that used for reducing $SiCl_4$ to SiH_4. However, the yield of germane, about 30% or less, was low compared with the essentially quantitative formation of silane from silicon tetrachloride. In an attempt to improve the yield of germane from the reaction between lithium aluminum hydride and germanium tetrachloride a variety of conditions were tested.[216] Best yield of germane (40%) is obtained by adding $GeCl_4$ solution in tetrahydrofuran to $LiAlH_4$ in tetrahydrofuran at 70°. A yellow or sometimes orange solid, probably $(GeH_2)_x$, is precipitated during the course of the reaction, but elemental germanium is not formed. This is in contrast to the reduction of $SnCl_4$ with $LiAlH_4$ when tin is formed.

Replacement of chlorine in $GeCl_4$ by hydrogen is very probably a stepwise process. Since the intermediate compounds, e.g., GeH_2Cl_2 are unstable (*vide infra*), forming $GeCl_2$ and other substances, side reactions are perhaps responsible for the poor yield of germane by the reduction process. The overall reaction scheme has been represented by,[216]

$$GeCl_4 \xrightarrow{LiAlH_4} GeHCl_3 \xrightarrow{LiAlH_4} GeH_2Cl_2 \xrightarrow{LiAlH_4} GeH_3Cl \xrightarrow{LiAlH_4} GeH_4$$

$$(GeH_2)_x \xleftarrow{LiAlH_4} GeCl_2 + Ge + HCl \xrightarrow{LiAlH_4} H_2$$

In the preparation of germane from germanium tetrachloride, lithium tri-t-butoxyaluminohydride is a much more efficient reducing agent than is lithium aluminum hydride.[304] With a relative concentration of Li$(t$-BuO$)_3$AlH to GeCl$_4$ of about 4.2, and in 30 hr. at room temperature, using tetrahydrofuran as solvent, germane may be obtained in 80% yield. Lithium tri-t-butoxyaluminohydride is a milder reducing agent than lithium aluminum hydride, and it has been suggested[304] that the high yield of germane in the above reaction is due to germanium tetrachloride being selectively reduced to GeH$_4$ rather than to germanium(II) chloride. Thus, the poor yield of GeH$_4$ when lithium aluminum hydride is used may not be due to any spontaneous decomposition of intermediates like GeH$_2$Cl$_2$, but to an immediate reduction of the Ge(IV) state to GeCl$_2$.*

A different approach to the preparation of germane is to use sodium borohydride to reduce germanium compounds. When an aqueous solution of sodium borohydride is added to an aqueous acidic solution of germanium oxide, germane is obtained in 73% yield.[252] In some reactions formation of trace amounts of digermane was observed, a fact noted more clearly in a later study.[172] This method for obtaining germane parallels a similar procedure for preparing stannane described below. In the case of germane a further extension of the method involved reducing germanium tetrachloride at ambient temperatures in aqueous medium with sodium borohydride.[217] A careful search for the most suitable reaction conditions finally led to formation of germane in 79% yield. Some germanium is produced during the reaction, indicating that the yield of germane is lowered by at least one side reaction, probably involving reduction of GeCl$_4$ to the free metal. If the reduction of GeCl$_4$ with NaBH$_4$ is carried out in tetrahydrofuran, only a low yield of GeH$_4$ is obtained. However, on addition of water an immediate evolution of

---

* It is well known that the valence state II becomes more stable in passing from C to Pb.

germane takes place.[217]   This fact, together with the behavior of sodium borohydride in other situations, suggests that production of germane takes place in two steps,

$$GeCl_4 + 4NaBH_4 \longrightarrow Ge(BH_4)_4 + 4NaCl$$

$$Ge(BH_4)_4 + 12H_2O \longrightarrow GeH_4 + 4B(OH)_3 + 12H_2$$

It can be seen from the foregoing remarks that the chemist now has available a variety of good methods for obtaining germane, and it is to be hoped that this will lead to a significant extension of our knowledge of the chemistry of this hitherto rare hydride.

The compound GeH_3Cl, the germanium analogue of the silicon compound SiH_3Cl, may be prepared by treating germane with hydrogen chloride in the presence of aluminum chloride at room temperature.[66] Some dichlorogermane GeH_2Cl_2 is always produced simultaneously in this reaction.   Similarly, treatment of germane with hydrogen bromide at room temperature in the presence of aluminum bromide affords GeH_3Br and GeH_2Br_2.[66]   For many years it appeared that GeH_3I must be very unstable since the end products of a reaction between monogermane and hydrogen iodide were reported to be GeI_2, H_2 and GeI_4 rather than GeH_3I.[66]   Furthermore, triiodomonogermane was found to be unstable above 0° and therefore was not definitely characterized.[38]   However, it has recently been found that germane and iodine react at room temperature to give germyl iodide, as well as diiodogermane (Table 7).[303]

Treatment of the compound GeH_3Br with silver fluoride at 25° affords GeH_3F, GeH_2F_2 and GeH_4.[289]   Since it is known that GeH_3F disproportionates slowly (15% decomposition after 16 hrs. at 25°), it can be assumed that the germane and difluorogermane are produced *via* GeH_3F as an intermediate.

The compound trichlorogermane was first prepared by Winkler[341] by passing hydrogen chloride over heated germanium or its sulfide.   At first[341] it was believed that the substance formed was $GeCl_2$, but later it was suggested that the compound was $GeHCl_3$.   It was not until the vacuum manipulation technique was used and a different mode of preparation, the action of hydrogen chloride upon germanium dichloride employed, that the composition and chemical properties of $GeHCl_3$ were established beyond doubt.[67]   The melting point of trichlorogermane was found to be $-71°$, and from extrapolation of the vapor pressure equation, the boiling point was given as $75.2°$.[67] However, because trichlorogermane loses hydrogen chloride readily at about $-30°$,[229] it is probable that the boiling point is only approximately correct. Later it was found that hydrogen chloride reacts with germanium monosulfide even in the absence of heating to form $GeHCl_3$.[229] This is a great advantage over the alternative procedure using HCl and $GeCl_2$, since the latter decomposes yielding sub-halides of germanium.

The compound tribromogermane $GeHBr_3$ (M.P. $-24°$) has been obtained from the reaction between hydrogen bromide and germanium dibromide.[342]

Organogermanes have been prepared by methods similar to those used to prepare organosilanes, e.g., reduction of organogermanium halides with complex metal hydrides, and by some methods not applicable to the preparation of silanes. Some examples illustrating the methods used are given below. In the case of the reactions involving lithium aluminum hydride some cleavage of the Ge—C bond usually occurs, with formation of germane.

$$CH_3GeCl_3 \xrightarrow{\text{LiAlH}_4} CH_3GeH_3 \tag{109}$$

$$CH_2{:}CHGeCl_3 \xrightarrow{\text{LiAlH}_4} CH_2{:}CHGeH_3 \tag{40}$$

$$(C_6H_5)_2GeCl_2 \xrightarrow{\text{LiAlH}_4} (C_6H_5)_2GeH_2 \tag{166}$$

$$n\text{-}C_3H_7GeCl_3 \xrightarrow{\text{LiAlH}_4} n\text{-}C_3H_7GeH_3 \tag{168}$$

$$H_3GeNa + RX \xrightarrow{\text{liquid NH}_3} RGeH_3 + NaX \tag{313}$$

$$R = CH_3,\ C_2H_5,\ n\text{-}C_3H_7$$

$$(C_2H_5)_3GeLi + NH_3 \xrightarrow{\text{liquid NH}_3} (C_2H_5)_3GeH + LiNH_2 \tag{184}$$

$$(C_6H_5)_3GeNa + NH_4Br \xrightarrow{\text{liquid NH}_3} (C_6H_5)_3GeH + NaBr + NH_3 \tag{185}$$

$$(C_6H_5)_3GeBr \xrightarrow[\text{HCl aqueous}]{\text{amalgamated Zn}} (C_6H_5)_3GeH \tag{332}$$

The last reaction is not known in silicon or tin chemistry, and it is consistent with the idea that germanium in many of its compounds is more electronegative than either silicon or tin.

B.   Properties of the Germanes

1. THE UNSUBSTITUTED GERMANES

The three volatile germanium hydrides GeH_4, Ge_2H_6 and Ge_3H_8 are thermally less stable than the silanes.   Monogermane decomposes measurably at about 280° into germanium and hydrogen, well over 100° below the temperature at which silane undergoes appreciable decomposition.

The decomposition of GeH_4 has been studied kinetically.[107,158,310] It has been proposed[107] that the initiating step for the homogeneous decomposition of germane is $GeH_4 \rightarrow GeH_2 + H_2$.   The GeH_2 is then further decomposed, but the mode of its decomposition is not clear.

Pyrolysis of digermane between 195° and 222° has also been the subject of a kinetic study.   The activation energy for pyrolysis was found to be 33.7 kcal.[87]

The hydrides GeH_4 and Ge_2H_6 are much less easily oxidized than their silicon analogues, SiH_4 and Si_2H_6.   The oxidation of monogermane and digermane has been studied analytically,[86] and in the presence of excess of oxygen may be represented by the equations,

$$GeH_4 + 2O_2 \longrightarrow GeO_2 + 2H_2O$$

$$2Ge_2H_6 + 7O_2 \longrightarrow 4GeO_2 + 6H_2O$$

Monogermane slowly reacts with oxygen at 160-183°, whereas digermane is rapidly oxidized at about 100°.

With alkali metals in liquid ammonia, germane undergoes the reaction,

$$GeH_4 + M \xrightarrow[NH_3]{liquid} H_3GeM + \tfrac{1}{2}H_2 \qquad (183, 313)$$

$$(M = K, Na)$$

The ammonia-free compounds $NaGeH_3$ and $KGeH_3$ are white air-sensitive solids, unstable at room temperature, $2H_3GeM \rightarrow 2MGe + 3H_2$.

Mention has been made previously of the reaction between H_3GeM compounds and alkyl halides which yields organogermanes.   It might have been thought from this that treatment of H_3GeM with CH_2Br_2 would afford the compound $CH_2(GeH_3)_2$.   This is not so; instead it has been stated that the reaction,

$$CH_2Br_2 + 2NaGeH_3 + NH_3 \longrightarrow CH_3GeH_3 + GeH_3NH_2 + 2NaBr$$

takes place, although the amino compound was not actually isolated.[313] With aromatic halides, sodium germyl does not afford phenylgermane but undergoes the reaction.[163]

$$NaGeH_3 + C_6H_5Br \longrightarrow C_6H_6 + GeH_2 + NaBr$$

The "dihydride" is soluble in liquid ammonia, but on removal of the ammonia the yellowish solid obtained disproportionates, $3GeH_2 \rightarrow GeH_4 + 2GeH$.[145]

Treatment of sodium germanide with ammonium bromide in liquid ammonia, followed by evaporation of the ammonia, affords a brown solid $(GeH)_x$.[183]

The dihydride $(GeH_2)_x$, mentioned above, has also been obtained by the reaction sequence,[260]

$$CaH_2 + Ge \xrightarrow{950°} CaGe + H_2$$
$$CaGe + 2HCl_{aq.} \longrightarrow CaCl_2 + (GeH_2)_x$$

It has been suggested that this dihydride is polymeric, and like other GeX_2 compounds may contain Ge—Ge bonds. With bromine it yields $GeBr_4$ and HBr, while with boiling aqueous HCl it yields H_2, Ge, GeH_4, Ge_2H_6 and Ge_3H_8. In the dry state $(GeH_2)_x$ is explosively oxidized by oxygen.

2. THE SUBSTITUTED GERMANES

The halogermanes decompose thermally more easily than the halosilanes. The disproportionation of germyl fluoride was mentioned above. Monochlorogermane decomposes slowly at room temperature into germane, hydrogen chloride and germanium. Dichlorogermane is even less stable than monochlorogermane.

The reactions between the halogermanes and ammonia or water do not parallel those between the halosilanes and these reagents. For example, monochlorogermane and ammonia are reported[68] to react according to the equation,

$$3xGeH_3Cl + 3xNH_3 \longrightarrow 3xNH_4Cl + xGeH_4 + 2(GeH)_x$$

No germanium analogues of $(SiH_3)_3N$ or $(SiH_3)_2O$ have yet been described. Thus germyl bromide does not react with silver oxide or mercuric oxide to yield $(GeH_3)_2O$, and although germyl iodide does react with the metal oxides, the volatile products are germane and water, formed apparently by the decomposition of digermyl ether.[303]   Germyl iodide, however, shows promise of being a very useful reagent in germanium chemistry since it reacts with mercury(II) sulfide to give digermyl sulfide, $(GeH_3)_2S$ (v.p. 0°/6 mm).

The direct reaction between GeH_3Cl and an excess of methylamine, dimethylamine, trimethylamine, triethylamine or pyridine at $-78°$ gives 1:1 adducts which decompose above $-78°$ into the yellow amorphous $(GeH_2)_x$ and the corresponding quaternary salt.[288]   Removal of hydrogen chloride from germyl chloride by methylamine or other amines should be contrasted with the reaction between silyl chloride and methylamine which yields $(SiH_3)_2NCH_3$.   This difference in behavior may be understood in terms of the greater electronegativity of a chlorine atom bound to germanium over that of a chlorine atom bound to silicon, making the hydrogen atoms in GeH_3Cl more likely to be lost as protons than those in SiH_3Cl.   In this connection it may be noted that although the "electronegativity" of germanium is very similar to that of silicon the dipole moment of GeH_3Cl (2.03D) is greater than that of SiH_3Cl (1.31D) suggesting that in a Ge—Cl linkage d_π—p_π bonding is less extensive than in an Si—Cl bond, in agreement with the suggestion[288] that chlorine would remove electron density more effectively from germanium than from silicon.

The behavior of GeH_2Cl_2 towards ammonia is similar to that of GeH_3Cl.   However, the initial product of the reaction between $GeHCl_3$ and ammonia appears to be a "diammoniate."   The fluoride GeH_3F behaves similarly, forming $GeH_3F, 2NH_3$ at $-78°$.[289]   This adduct releases a mole of ammonia at 25° to give a non-volatile white solid which decomposes without melting at 180°.   The "monoammoniate" may be the salt $(GeH_3NH_3)F$.

The organogermanes, a number of which are listed in Table 7, undergo several types of reaction also observed in organosilane chemistry.   However, before reviewing a few such reactions, it is convenient to summarize briefly properties of the germanes which set these hydrides apart from the silanes and, to a somewhat lesser extent, from the stannanes.   Indeed, in some reactions the stannanes resemble the silanes more closely than they do the germanes.

The following chemical observations make the behavior of the germanes appear anomalous unless it is accepted that the electronegativity of germanium in germanes is greater than that of silicon in the silanes or tin in the stannanes.

(1) The relative inertness of the germanes to oxidation, i.e., the Ge—H linkage is a less powerful reducing agent than the Si—H or Sn—H.

(2) The relative inertness of the germanes to decomposition on treatment with base.

(3) Reduction of organogermanium halides with zinc and hydrochloric acid to organogermanes. This does not occur with organosilicon halides or organotin halides although the latter may be reduced with aluminum in *neutral* solution (Chap. IV. Sec. A).

(4) The anomalous reaction of the Ge—H linkage with RLi compounds (Chap. IV. Sec. B).

One reaction common to organo-germanium and -silicon chemistry involves addition of the M—H bond to carbon—carbon double bonds:

$$RCH:CH_2 + GeHCl_3 \xrightarrow[\text{catalyst}]{\text{peroxide}} RCH_2CH_2GeCl_3 \qquad (112, 257)$$

Some peroxide-catalyzed addition reactions of triphenylgermane and trialkylgermanes have also been described.[130,139,220a] It is interesting that triphenylgermane adds to unsaturated linkages with a greater facility than does triphenylsilane. Indeed, it has recently been found that triphenylgermane will add to a number of organic compounds containing olefinic double bonds in the absence of solvent and catalyst. In this way organogermanium compounds containing functional groups may be synthesized.[155a]

$$(C_6H_5)_3GeH + CH_2:CHY \xrightarrow{\text{heat}} (C_6H_5)_3GeCH_2CH_2Y$$

$$(Y = C_6H_5, CN, OCOCH_3, CONH_2, COCH_3, CONH_2, etc.)$$

Addition reactions of M^{IV}—H (M^{IV} = Si, Ge or Sn) bonds to carbon—carbon double bonds raises the question of the degree of stability of molecules possessing both $C = C$ and M^{IV}—H linkages. In this connection it has been found that organosilanes having vinyl and hydrogen joined to the same silicon atom may be polymerized using platinum catalysts to yield polymers wherein silicon atoms are connected through —(CH_2CH_2)— bridges.[60] Moreover, the compound vinylsilane polymerizes rapidly when irradiated with ultraviolet light.[335] In order to determine the ease of polymerization when both a vinyl group and a hydrogen atom are bonded to germanium, the compound vinylgermane was prepared.[40] It was found that this compound was much less stable than vinylsilane. Vinylgermane polymerizes fairly readily to a white solid in daylight, especially in the presence of mercury. The infrared spectrum of polyvinylgermane is similar to that of polyvinylsilane, and the two polymers probably have similar structures, $—(CH_2CH_2MH_2)_x—$, where M = Si or Ge. Vinylstannane is even less stable than vinyl-germane, and must be stored at low temperatures to avoid decomposition.[40]

In common with Si—H bonds, or for that matter Sn—H bonds, the Ge—H bond possesses reducing properties. Triethylgermane reduces the salts of many transition elements either to a lower oxidation state, or sometimes to the free metal, and is itself converted to $(C_2H_5)_3GeX$ type compounds.[7] Similarly, $n\text{-}C_4H_9GeH_2Cl$, $n\text{-}C_4H_9GeH_2Br$, $n\text{-}C_4H_9GeH_2I$, $(n\text{-}C_4H_9)_2GeHCl$, $(n\text{-}C_4H_9)_2GeHBr$, $(n\text{-}C_4H_9)_2GeHI$, $(n\text{-}C_4H_9)_2GeHNCS$ and $(n\text{-}C_4H_9)_2GeHCN$ form easily through gradual addition of $HgCl_2$, $HgBr_2$, I_2, $Hg(SCN)_2$ or $Hg(CN)_2$ to an excess of the appropriate n-butylgermane.[10]

Methylgermanes react with hydrogen chloride in the presence of aluminum chloride, e.g.,[6]

$$CH_3GeH_3 \xrightarrow[20°]{\text{HCl and AlCl}_3} CH_3GeH_2Cl \longrightarrow CH_3GeHCl_2$$

Similar substitution reactions involving alkylsilanes have previously been described.

The alkylgermanes react with alkali metals in liquid ammonia in a manner similar to monogermane or the alkylstannanes discussed in the next chapter, but the reaction products are not clear-cut.[145]

3. SOME PHYSICOCHEMICAL STUDIES MADE ON COMPOUNDS CONTAINING Ge—H BONDS

Determinations of the heat capacity, heat of fusion and vaporization, moment of inertia and entropy of monogermane have been made.[54] The heats of formation of germane (ΔH_f°, 21.6 ± 0.5 kcal. mole^{-1}) and diger-mane (ΔH_f°, 38.7 ± 0.3 kcal. mole^{-1}) have been determined from the heats of decomposition of mixtures of the hydrides with stibine.[149] The results lead to the thermochemical bond energies Ge—H 69.0 kcal., and

Ge—Ge 37.9 kcal.   It is interesting to compare the latter value with the activation energy of 33.7 kcal. for pyrolysis of digermane mentioned above.   It had earlier been assumed[279] that this activation energy represented the Ge—Ge bond energy.   However, for the reason given earlier during discussion of the pyrolytic data for Si_2H_6, it is not safe to regard activation energies for the decomposition of hydrides M_2H_6 as being equal to the M—M thermochemical bond energy.

Germane and its derivatives have been the subject of a number of spectroscopic studies.   The Raman spectrum of liquid GeH_4 has been investigated.[266]   An early study of the infrared spectrum of germane led to a value of 1.48 Å for the Ge—H bond distance.[301]   However, this value is not in good agreement with the value of the Ge—H bond length in halogermanes obtained from microwave studies.   This is not surprising, since in common with other tetrahedral molecules analysis of the infrared spectrum of GeH_4 is complicated by strong Coriolis perturbations.   As mentioned previously, a similar difficulty occurred in analysis of the spectrum of silane.   As in the case of silane, the difficulty has been circumvented by analyzing the spectra of deutero-compounds, *viz.* GeH_3D and $GeHD_3$, where only one band need be analyzed and no perturbations occur with the Ge—D stretching mode.[201]   In this manner the germanium-hydrogen distance obtained was 1.52 Å, assuming that it is unchanged by isotopic substitution.   In a continuation of this work the infrared and Raman spectra for GeD_4, GeD_3H, GeD_2H_2 and $GeDH_3$ have been obtained, and an assignment of fundamentals has been made.[202] The infrared spectra of GeH_3Cl,[211] GeD_3Cl,[211] $GeHCl_3$[203] and $GeDCl_3$[203] have also been studied.

A microwave study of GeH_3Cl yielded a Ge—H distance of 1.52 Å,[61,220] while a similar investigation of $GeHCl_3$ gave 1.55 ± 0.04 Å.[324]   These values are in excellent agreement with the Ge—H distance obtained from the infrared study referred to earlier.[201]   In the microwave technique larger limits of error occur because only the small moment of inertia is obtained and this is fairly insensitive to the Ge—H distance.   A study[147a] of the microwave spectrum of germyl fluoride has yielded the following parameters for this molecule: Ge—H = 1.52 Å; Ge—F = 1.73 Å; < HGeH = 109°54'.   As a result of this work, sufficient microwave data is now available to permit a comparison of M—X bond distances in all molecules of type MH_3X (M = Si or Ge; X = F, Cl, or Br).   The differences between the sums of the covalent radii and the observed internuclear bond distances for these compounds suggests that germanium is less effective than silicon in M—X d_π—p_π bonding.[147a]

$$r_M + r_X - d(\text{M—X}), \text{ in Å}$$

X	F	Cl	Br
SiH₃X	0.295	0.11	0.10
GeH₃X	0.21	0.06	0.06

It would appear, however, that halogen-germanium dative π-bonding, using $4d$ orbitals of germanium and non-bonding p-electrons of the halogen atoms, does occur to some extent, especially with the electronegative fluorine atom.

The microwave spectrum of methylgermane has been examined.[196a] Among the parameters obtained were: Ge—H = 1.529 ± 0.005 Å; Ge—C = 1.9453 ± 0.0005 Å; < HGeH = 109° 15′ ± 30′.   The internal barrier to rotation about the carbon-germanium bond was estimated to be 1239 cal. mole⁻¹.   Thus, as might be expected because the M^{IV}—C bonds increase in length, the barriers to internal rotation in ethane, methylsilane and methylgermane are 2.88, 1.67 and 1.24 kcal. mole⁻¹ respectively, decreasing qualitatively as the size of M^{IV} increases.

An electron diffraction study has been made of Ge_2H_6 and Ge_3H_8[246] in order to obtain information on the covalent radius of germanium.   The Ge—Ge bond distance in both molecules was found to be 2.41 ± 0.02 Å. With new electron diffraction techniques this bond distance could probably be obtained more accurately.

The infrared spectra of gaseous and solid Ge_2H_6 have been investigated,[76] band assignments made, and the barrier to internal rotation estimated as 1.2 kcal.   As mentioned previously, the barrier to internal rotation in Si_2H_6 has been estimated as about 1 kcal.   In view of the longer Ge—Ge distance in Ge_2H_6 compared with the Si—Si distance in Si_2H_6, it is surprising that the barriers to internal rotation in the two molecules are the same.   It would appear that a more accurate study is called for.

The mass spectra of mono- and digermane have been studied and the results for germane have been used to calculate a D(Ge—H) value of 54.5 kcal. mole⁻¹ [319]

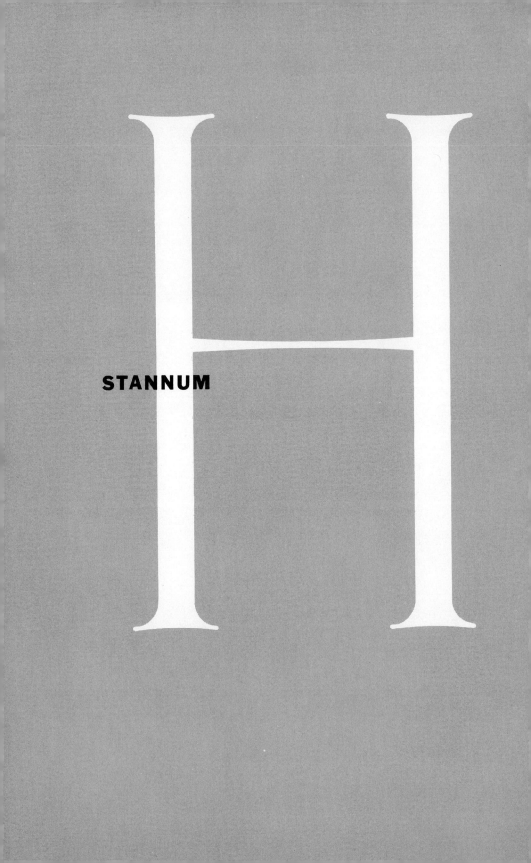

STANNUM

STANNANE

AND ITS DERIVATIVES

For many years stannane, SnH_4, was the only known volatile binary tin-hydrogen compound, but as described below the highly unstable distannane has recently been discovered. Several organostannanes, R_nSnH_{4-n} (n = 1, 2, or 3), are known, but these are thermally much less stable than their germanium or silicon analogues. Until very recently the existence of halo-derivatives of stannane similar to such compounds as SiH_3Cl or GeH_2Br_2 had not been demonstrated. All this reflects the low affinity of tin for hydrogen, the poor stability of SnH_4 making it difficult to use this hydride as an intermediate in the synthesis of other compounds.

A. Preparation of the Stannanes

Stannane was first obtained by treating a tin-magnesium alloy with dilute acids, by adding magnesium powder to tin dissolved in sulfuric acid and by the electrolytic reduction of tin solutions using lead electrodes.[240,241] The yield of stannane in all these reactions is very poor, the hydride being formed only a few milligrams at a time. The discovery that lithium aluminum hydride will reduce tin tetrachloride to stannane has made the tin hydride much more readily available.[111] However, the yield of stannane in this reaction, about 20%, is poor when compared with the yields of other hydrides obtained when the appropriate covalent halides (e.g., $SiCl_4$ or BCl_3) are treated with lithium aluminum hydride. It has been suggested that the comparatively low yield of stannane is due to reduction of Sn(IV) to Sn(II), the aluminohydrides of these oxidation states being reaction intermediates.[337]

$$SnCl_4 + 4LiAlH_4 \longrightarrow Sn(AlH_4)_4 + 4LiCl$$

$$Sn(AlH_4)_4 \longrightarrow SnH_4 + 4AlH_3$$

$$Sn(AlH_4)_4 \longrightarrow Sn(AlH_4)_2 + H_2 + 2AlH_3$$

$$Sn(AlH_4)_2 \longrightarrow Sn + H_2 + 2AlH_3$$

However, this idea may not be correct. As discussed below, the decomposition of stannane to tin and hydrogen is strongly inhibited by the presence of traces of oxygen. Consequently, it was found that when reduction of tin tetrachloride with lithium aluminum hydride is carried out in the presence of a little oxygen, stannane is obtained in 80-90% yield.[88] The high yield of the hydride when reduction is carried out in the presence of oxygen suggests that decomposition of stannane itself is the most important side reaction responsible for the poor yield in the absence of oxygen.

Before the variables in the tin tetrachloride-lithium aluminum hydride reaction were worked out, however, another convenient method for obtaining stannane was discovered. If tin(II) chloride in aqueous solution is treated with an aqueous solution of sodium borohydride, stannane is obtained in 84% yield based on tin used.[262,264] A later study of this reaction has indicated certain subtleties.[172] An improved yield in terms of borohydride consumed is obtained by adding a solution of potassium borohydride and stannite ion to acid. Besides stannane the new hydride Sn_2H_6 is formed.[171,172] When a trap containing distannane is allowed to warm to room temperature, the hydride completely decomposes into tin and hydrogen. Distannane may be distilled in a vacuum system without decomposition provided relatively low pressures are used.

TABLE 8. THE STANNANES.

Compound	B.P.	Reference	Compound	B.P.	Reference
SnH₄*	−52°	220	(n-C₃H₇)₂SnH₂	40°/12 mm	321
CH₃SnH₃	0°	88,111	(n-C₃H₇)₃SnH	76-82°/12 mm	321
(CH₃)₂SnH₂	35°	111,179	n-C₄H₉SnH₃	100°	321
(CH₃)₃SnH	60°/750 mm	111	(n-C₄H₉)₂SnH₂	75°/12 mm	321
C₂H₅SnH₃	35°	73	(n-C₄H₉)₃SnH	76-81°/0.8 mm	321
(C₂H₅)₂SnH₂	99°	73	(C₆H₅)₃SnH	168-172°/0.5 mm	321
(C₂H₅)₃SnH	142°	73			

* M.P. −150°.

Several organostannanes have been prepared by methods similar to those used to prepare organogermanes, e.g.,

$$CH_3SnCl_3 \xrightarrow{\text{LiAlH}_4} CH_3SnH_3 \tag{111}$$

$$(C_2H_5)_3SnI \xrightarrow{\text{LiAlH}_4} (C_2H_5)_3SnH \tag{8}$$

$$(C_2H_5)_2SnCl_2 \xrightarrow{\text{LiAlH}_4} (C_2H_5)_2SnH_2 \tag{73}$$

$$(C_6H_5)_3SnCl \xrightarrow{\text{LiAlH}_4} (C_6H_5)_3SnH \tag{137}$$

$$(n\text{-}C_3H_7)_2SnCl_2 \xrightarrow{\text{LiAlH}_4} (n\text{-}C_3H_7)_2SnH_2 \tag{321}$$

$$R_3SnNa + NH_4Br \xrightarrow{\text{liquid NH}_3} R_3SnH + NaBr + NH_3 \tag{51, 186}$$
$$(R = CH_3 \text{ or } C_6H_5)$$

$$R_3SnCl \xrightarrow[\text{Al and water}]{\text{amalgamated}} R_3SnH \tag{322}$$
$$(R = C_3H_7, C_4H_9, \text{ etc.})$$

B. Properties of the Stannanes

Stannane undergoes appreciable decomposition into tin and hydrogen even at ordinary temperatures. Above 100° it is very rapidly decomposed. The decomposition reaction has been the subject of kinetic studies.[179a,309] It is first order with respect to stannane, being independent of the hydrogen pressure. The very interesting observation was made that a small amount of oxygen can stop the decomposition by forming an oxide film on the tin surface, upon which decomposition of the hydride takes place.[309]

Stannane is not affected by dilute acids or alkalis, but it is decomposed by strongly alkaline or acidic solutions. It is intermediate in behavior in this respect between silane and germane. Stannane is a reducing agent, being decomposed by solutions of transition metal salts. The hydride is toxic.

Treatment of stannane with hydrogen chloride affords hydrogen and the highly unstable compound SnH_3Cl. The latter detectably decomposes at $-70°$.[4]

$$2SnH_3Cl \xrightarrow{-2HCl} 2SnH_2 \longrightarrow SnH_4 + Sn$$

$$SnH_4 + 2HCl \xrightarrow{-2H_2} SnH_2Cl_2 \longrightarrow SnCl_2 + H_2$$

In contrast, GeH_3Cl is reasonably stable up to $20°$ and SiH_3Cl up to $200°$.

It is possible to titrate sodium in liquid ammonia with stannane to form, with liberation of hydrogen, an ammonia solution of H_3SnNa.[88] At first H_2SnNa_2 is formed, but on addition of more hydride H_3SnNa is produced. Removal of the ammonia at $-63.5°$ leads to blackening with loss of hydrogen, decomposition of the solid H_3SnNa becoming rapid at about $0°$. It appears that H_3SnNa, like H_3GeNa, is stable only as an ammine. Stannylsodium (compare H_3GeNa) reacts with alkyl iodides at $-63.5°$ in ammonia to form alkylstannanes and sodium iodide.[88] Just as GeH_4 can be regenerated from H_3GeNa by adding NH_4Cl,[183] so SnH_4 can be formed by adding a solution of NH_4Cl in ammonia to H_3SnNa in the same solvent.[88]

As expected from the stability of tetraalkyl- and tetraaryltin compounds, and the instability of stannane, the stability of organotin hydrides increases with decreasing number of tin-hydrogen linkages in the molecule.[73] In general, a trialkyltin hydride is only very slightly decomposed after months at ambient temperatures, providing air and moisture are excluded, and may be distilled at reduced pressure in an inert atmosphere. Triphenyltin hydride is thermally much less stable, although it may be distilled under reduced pressure.[137] It is decomposed to some extent on exposure to light. Diphenyltin dihydride is decomposed by heating *in vacuo* above $100°$.

$$(C_6H_5)_2SnH_2 \longrightarrow (C_6H_5)_2Sn + H_2$$

$$2(C_6H_5)_2Sn \longrightarrow (C_6H_5)_4Sn + Sn$$

Diphenyltin dihydride decomposes in the presence of amines to give yellow modifications of diphenyltin polymer. If the hydride in ether solution is treated with methanol, slow gas evolution occurs to give a colorless diphenyltin polymer. The latter, unlike the yellow form, is soluble in benzene and its molecular weight indicates a degree of polymerization of five or six.[192a] Phenyltin trihydride has not been prepared as yet. *n*-Butyltin trihydride, on the other hand, can be distilled at its normal boiling point (100°) under nitrogen, although it is pyrolyzed to some extent. At ambient temperatures, n-$C_4H_9SnH_3$ releases a yellowish brown precipitate after a few hours.

Organostannanes are fairly easily oxidized. In contact with air $(C_6H_5)_3SnH$ rapidly forms $(C_6H_5)_6Sn_2$, while $(C_2H_5)_2SnH_2$ is decomposed explosively in a stream of oxygen. In the presence of atmospheric oxygen at room temperature organostannanes release a grayish-white precipitate.

Just as stannane reacts with sodium in liquid ammonia so do the organostannanes.[179] It is possible to titrate a solution of sodium in liquid ammonia with dimethylstannane so as to form the species $(CH_3)_2SnNa_2$, $(CH_3)_2SnHNa$, $[(CH_3)_2SnNa]_2$ and even $(CH_3)_2(NH_2)SnNa$.

The chemistry of the organotin hydrides has been investigated more throughly than that of the organogermanes. Important reactions of the organostannanes include the following:

At room temperature organotin hydrides are completely decomposed by ethereal or alcoholic solutions of hydrogen halides with quantitative evolution of hydrogen. This reaction is suitable for quantitative determination of organotin hydrides. Organic acids react with the hydrides in a similar manner. Thus $(n$-$C_3H_7)_3SnH$ and $(C_6H_5)_3SnH$ with acetic acid yield triorganotin acetates.[236]

With alcoholic base, R_3SnH compounds are converted to R_3SnOH and hydrogen.

Organotin hydrides react vigorously with halogens, in a manner similar to the organosilanes, e.g.,

$$(n\text{-}C_3H_7)_3SnH + Br_2 \longrightarrow (n\text{-}C_3H_7)_3SnBr + HBr.$$

Organostannanes undergo a number of hydrogen-halogen exchange reactions, e.g.,

$$(C_2H_5)_3SnH + AgBr \longrightarrow (C_2H_5)_3SnBr + Ag + \tfrac{1}{2}H_2 \qquad (8)$$

$$4(C_2H_5)_3SnH + 3HgCl_2 \longrightarrow 4(C_2H_5)_3SnCl + Hg + Hg_2Cl_2 + 2H_2 \quad (8)$$

$$3(n\text{-}C_3H_7)_3SnH + AlCl_3 \longrightarrow 3(n\text{-}C_3H_7)_3SnCl + Al + \tfrac{3}{2}H_2 \qquad (236)$$

$$(n\text{-}C_3H_7)_3SnH \xrightarrow{R_2O \cdot BF_3} (n\text{-}C_3H_7)_3SnF \qquad (236)$$

$$(C_6H_5)_3SnH + CH_2{:}CHCH_2Br \longrightarrow (C_6H_5)_3SnBr + CH_3CH{:}CH_2 \qquad (320)$$

$$(n\text{-}C_4H_9)_2SnH_2 + (n\text{-}C_4H_9)_2SnCl_2 \longrightarrow 2(n\text{-}C_4H_9)_2SnHCl \qquad (263a)$$

The last reaction, it should be noted, affords a substance in which a hydrogen atom and a chlorine atom are simultaneously bonded to tin. Apart from the highly unstable SnH_3Cl mentioned earlier, $(n\text{-}C_4H_9)_2SnHCl$ is the only compound of this type known. On distillation at reduced pressure di-n-butylchlorotin hydride reverts to di-n-butyltin dichloride and di-n-butyltin dihydride.

Organotin hydrides reduce a number of organo-functional groups. These reductions do not proceed *via* an intermediate metal alkoxide and, therefore, require no hydrolysis step, in contrast to reductions with complex metal hydrides. For this reason, organotin hydrides may perhaps find some use as reagents in organic chemistry. Typical reactions include,

$$C_6H_5NO_2 + 6(C_6H_5)_3SnH \longrightarrow 3(C_6H_5)_6Sn_2 + C_6H_5NH_2 + 2H_2O \quad (236)$$

$$(C_4H_9)_2SnH_2 + C_6H_5COCH_3 \longrightarrow \frac{1}{x}[(C_4H_9)_2Sn]_x$$
$$+ C_6H_5CH(OH)CH_3 \quad (192)$$

$$(C_6H_5)_2SnH_2 + CH_2{:}CHCOCH_3 \longrightarrow \frac{1}{x}[(C_6H_5)_2Sn]_x$$
$$+ CH_2{:}CHCH(OH)CH_3 \quad (192)$$

$$(C_6H_5)_3SnH + C_6H_5COCl \longrightarrow (C_6H_5)_3SnCl + C_6H_5CHO \quad (236)$$

$$2(C_6H_5)_3SnH + C_6H_5CHO \longrightarrow (C_6H_5)_3SnSn(C_6H_5)_3$$
$$+ C_6H_5CH_2OH \quad (192)$$

A further interesting reaction of organotin hydrides occurs with diazomethane and its derivatives. Indeed, reactions with diazomethane are even more facile than those between diazomethane and organotin halides.[197]

$$R_3SnH + CH_2N_2 \longrightarrow R_3SnCH_3 + N_2$$
$$R_3SnH + N_2CHR' \longrightarrow R_3SnCH_2R' + N_2$$
$$(R = \text{alkyl, and } R' = COOC_2H_5, CN, COCH_3, COC_6H_5.)$$

As far as organotin chemistry is concerned, perhaps the most important reaction of the organotin hydrides is their ability to add to unsaturated carbon — carbon bonds,[320,323] making possible the synthesis of a wide variety of organotin compounds. As mentioned previously, this property is also common to the Si—H and Ge—H linkages. However, the reaction of the Sn—H bond with C=C or C≡C is distinctly different from reactions of these functional groups with Si—H or Ge—H, in that the Sn—H bond will add to unsaturated linkages *at moderate temperatures* even in the absence of peroxide or other catalysts. Indeed, it is fortunate that no catalyst is required since the Sn—H bond is decomposed by ultraviolet light and peroxides. It is apparent that addition of Sn—H to unsaturated linkages does not proceed *via* a free radical mechanism but proceeds probably by an ionic mechanism. Thus triphenyltin hydride adds to styrene even in the presence of hydroquinone, an inhibitor of free radical reactions.

Addition reactions of organotin hydrides to olefinic compounds are affected in only a few instances by the presence of other functional groups in the olefin. One such case, the reduction of methyl vinyl ketone to methyl vinyl carbinol, has been mentioned above.

Reaction of a triorganostannane with an olefinic compound may be represented by[320,323]

$$R_3SnH + CH_2{:}CHR' \longrightarrow R_3SnC_2H_4R'$$

$$(R' = C_6H_5,\ CN,\ COOH,\ COOCH_3,\ Si(C_6H_5)_3,\ OH,\ OC_6H_5,\ CH_2CN,\ etc.)$$

Triphenylstannane is more reactive than trialkylstannanes in these addition reactions. Treatment of organotin monohydrides with substituted acetylenes in the correct proportions affords organotin compounds containing substituted vinyl groups:

$$R_3SnH + CH{:}CR' \longrightarrow R_3SnCH{:}CHR'$$
$$(R = C_6H_5 \text{ or } n\text{-}C_3H_7,\ and\ R' = C_6H_5 \text{ or } CH_2OH)$$

In a reaction of this type acetylene and tri-*n*-butyltin hydride afford tri-*n*-butylvinyltin in 75-80% yield.[282] With excess of organotin hydride di-addition products may be obtained.

Compounds of the type R_2SnH_2 and $RSnH_3$ react with olefinic compounds to give organotin derivatives containing two or three functionally substituted alkyl groups. This type of reaction is somewhat limited by the thermal instability of the tin hydride starting materials. However, if only limited heating of reagents is required for reactions, useful products can be isolated,[156,157,320] e.g.,

$$C_4H_9SnH_3 + 3CH_2{:}CHCOOCH_3 \longrightarrow C_4H_9Sn(CH_2CH_2COOCH_3)_3$$

$$(C_3H_7)_2SnH_2 + 2CH_2{:}CHC_6H_5 \longrightarrow (C_3H_7)_2Sn(CH_2CH_2C_6H_5)_2$$

$$(C_6H_5)_3SnH + (C_6H_5)_3MCH{:}CH_2 \longrightarrow (C_6H_5)_3SnCH_2CH_2M(C_6H_5)_3$$
$$(M = Si,\ Ge,\ Sn)$$

$$2(C_6H_5)_3SnH + (C_6H_5)_2M(CH:CH_2)_2 \longrightarrow$$
$$(M = Si, Ge)$$

$$\begin{array}{c} C_6H_5 \\ | \\ (C_6H_5)_3SnCH_2CH_2MCH_2CH_2Sn(C_6H_5)_3 \\ | \\ C_6H_5 \end{array}$$

$$(C_6H_5)_2SnH_2 + (C_6H_5)_3MCH:CH_2 \longrightarrow (C_6H_5)_3SnCH_2CH_2M(C_6H_5)_3*$$
$$(M = Si, Ge, Sn)$$

$$(C_6H_5)_2SnH_2 + (CH_2:CH)_2M(C_6H_5)_2 \longrightarrow (C_6H_5)_2Sn \underset{CH_2CH_2}{\overset{CH_2CH_2}{\diagdown \diagup}} M(C_6H_5)_2$$
$$(M = Si, Ge)$$

The formation of cyclic compounds in the latter reaction indicates that ring closure of the intermediate H—$Sn(C_6H_5)_2CH_2CH_2(C_6H_5)_2M$—$CH:CH_2$ occurs in preference to polymerization, although some polymerization does occur. An especially novel reaction between a tin hydride and an olefin involves di-n-butyltin dihydride and tetrafluoroethylene,[188]

$$(C_4H_9)_2SnH_2 + 2CF_2:CF_2 \xrightarrow{90°} (C_4H_9)_2Sn(CF_2CF_2H)_2$$

It has already been mentioned that triphenylsilane, or for that matter organosilanes in general, can be alkylated by alkyllithium compounds with formation of lithium hydride. Similarly, it has been found that triphenylstannane reacts with organolithium compounds,

$$(C_6H_5)_3SnH + RLi \longrightarrow (C_6H_5)_3SnR + LiH \qquad (142, 143)$$
$$(R = CH_3 \text{ or } C_6H_5)$$

In reactions with RLi compounds the hydrogen of the Si—H or Sn—H groups behaves as a *pseudo*-halogen in accord with a bond polarity $\overset{+}{M} - \overset{-}{H}$, leading to removal of the hydrogen as hydride ion. Organogermanes, however, behave differently from organosilanes or organostannanes with organolithium reagents. Although when $(C_6H_5)_3GeH$ is added to a refluxing ether solution of excess of C_6H_5Li tetraphenylgermane is isolated, reverse addition of excess C_6H_5Li to $(C_6H_5)_3GeH$ affords 50-60% yields of $(C_6H_5)_6Ge_2$.[167] It has been suggested[167] that the latter

---

* The nature of the product is understandable if the reasonable assumption is made that diphenyltin dihydride decomposes into triphenyltin hydride, and that it is the latter hydride which undergoes addition.

arises through the presence of triphenylgermyllithium, so that the reactions

$$C_6H_5Li + (C_6H_5)_3GeH \longrightarrow (C_6H_5)_3GeLi + C_6H_6$$

$$(C_6H_5)_3GeLi + (C_6H_5)_3GeH \longrightarrow (C_6H_5)_6Ge_2 + LiH$$

compete with

$$C_6H_5Li + (C_6H_5)_3GeH \longrightarrow (C_6H_5)_4Ge + LiH$$

It has since been found possible to prepare triphenylgermyllithium by treating triphenylgermane *with an equivalent amount* of an organolithium compound.[138]

Thus in its reactions with organolithium reagents triphenylgermane behaves more like $(C_6H_5)_3CH$, which is known to react with RLi compounds to give $(C_6H_5)_3CLi$, than $(C_6H_5)_3SiH$ or $(C_6H_5)_3SnH$. This is in accordance with the idea that the germanium—hydrogen bond is less polar in the sense $\overset{+}{Ge}$—$\overset{-}{H}$ than $\overset{+}{Si}$—$\overset{-}{H}$ or $\overset{+}{Sn}$—$\overset{-}{H}$, and is in agreement with the idea that germanium is not only more electronegative than tin, as expected, but is also more electronegative than silicon in some of its compounds (see Chap. III. Sec. B. 2).

As yet relatively few physicochemical studies have been made on stannane or the organostannanes presumably because until recently these compounds have been rather inaccessible.

An analysis of the Sn—H stretching vibration of $SnHD_3$, assuming the hydride is tetrahedral, has permitted determination of the Sn—H distance as 1.701 ± 0.001 Å.[339] This value is in very good agreement with that of 1.700 ± 0.015 Å derived from an analysis of the microwave spectrum of CH_3SnH_3 (C_{3v} structure).[200]

The infrared spectrum of undeuterated stannane has been reported.[218] The spectrum was used to calculate the thermodynamic functions of the hydride, and to estimate the bond dissociation energy as 73.7 kcal. mole^{-1}. This infrared study also led to an Sn—H distance of 1.76 Å.* This internuclear distance compares less favorably with the result obtained from

---

* Now that infrared studies have been carried out on all the Group IV hydrides MH_4 an interesting comparison of the M—H force constants can be made:[79] C—H, 5.4; Si—H, 3.0; Ge—H, 2.8; Sn—H, 1.7 md/Å. The decrease in M—H force constant with increasing atomic number of M agrees with the observation that the thermal stability of the hydrides falls in the same order.

the microwave spectrum of methylstannane than does the value from the earlier infrared work.[339] This is not surprising because an analysis of the spectrum of SnH_4, as opposed to analysis of a deuterated stannane, would be complicated by Coriolis perturbations (see page 53).

The mass spectrum of stannane has been studied[262] and the appearance potential of Sn^+ in the process

$$SnH_4 \longrightarrow Sn^+ + 4H^\circ_{(g)} + e^-$$

measured. Since the spectrographic ionization potential for the Sn^+ ion is known it has been possible to calculate the mean dissociation energy for the Sn—H bond as 70.3 ± 1.2 kcal. mole^{-1}. This result is in fair agreement with the value estimated from the infrared study, mentioned above. However, recently the heat of explosive decomposition of stannane-stibine mixtures has been measured[149] and the result used to calculate $\Delta H^\circ_f(SnH_4)$ as $+38.9$ kcal. mole^{-1}. From this the Sn—H thermochemical bond energy is derived as 60.4 kcal.

H

PLUMBUM

F I V E

LEAD HYDRIDES

With lead at the end of Group IV the metal—hydrogen bond is exceedingly weak. Because of this, plumbane has only been prepared in trace amounts and its physical constants, apart from its boiling point estimated as $-13°$, are unknown. The structure is presumably one in which there is a tetrahedral configuration of hydrogen atoms about a central lead atom.

Plumbane has been prepared by electrolyzing a sulfuric acid solution with lead electrodes. Minute quantities of PbH_4 along with hydrogen are obtained. The gas is also formed in trace amounts when a lead-magnesium alloy is dissolved in dilute acid.[243] In the early work the amount of PbH_4 formed was so small that the existence of the hydride could only be demonstrated by using radioactive lead in its preparation so as to obtain a gas, the radioactivity of which could be detected. The new metal hydride reducing agents have as yet been of little help in making PbH_4 more accessible. When divalent lead is treated with sodium borohydride, no plumbane is formed,[252] nor is the lead hydride formed when lead tetrachloride is treated with lithium aluminum hydride; only lead is produced.[88] Furthermore, in early work with lithium aluminum hydride, alkyllead halides were treated with the double hydride but no alkyllead hydrides were obtained.[111] Recently, however, it has been found possible to form trimethyllead hydride, triethyllead hydride, dimethyllead dihydride and diethyllead dihydride by reducing the corresponding chlorides with lithium aluminum hydride in dimethyl ether at very low temperatures,[5,26] e.g., $-78°$.[26] Trimethyllead hydride (M.P. $\sim -106°$) and triethyllead hydride (M.P. $-145°$), isolated in 95 and 20% yield, respectively, were characterized,[26] and were found to decompose according to the equation

$$4R_3PbH \longrightarrow 2H_2 + 3PbR_4 + Pb$$

Gas evolution from triethyllead hydride does not occur until the compound is warmed to about $-20°$, and it was observed that trimethyllead hydride does not release hydrogen until about $-30°$. Even at $0°$ complete decomposition of these two hydrides requires several hours. Upon exposure to air trimethyllead hydride will detonate, indicating that the organolead hydrides are hazardous materials. In the absence of air trimethyllead hydride was found to be sufficiently stable to react with the diazoalkane $CH_3CH_2N_2$, and with ethylene in diglyme at $0°$ and 500 p.s.i., to give trimethylethyllead. As discussed previously such reactions are also characteristic of tin—hydrogen bonds.

Trimethyllead hydride appears to have been obtained before publication of the work described above, but the stability and mode of decomposition of the hydride first reported[77] are somewhat different from those found in the later work.[26] When trimethyllead chloride and potassium borohydride are mixed in liquid ammonia at $-33°$ potassium chloride is precipitated suggesting the occurrence of the reaction

$$(CH_3)_3PbCl + KBH_4 \xrightarrow{\text{liquid NH}_3} (CH_3)_3PbBH_4 + KCl$$

After removal of the ammonia solvent and warming the residue to $-5°$, a material was obtained which condensed at liquid nitrogen temperature. This condensate contained no boron, melted at about $-100°$ to a colorless liquid, and was presumably trimethyllead hydride formed by the reaction

$$NH_3 + (CH_3)_3PbBH_4 \xrightarrow{-5°} (CH_3)_3PbH + H_3NBH_3$$

With hydrogen chloride, hydrogen and trimethyllead chloride were produced in agreement with the equation

$$(CH_3)_3PbH + HCl \longrightarrow (CH_3)_3PbCl + H_2.$$

However, the trimethyllead hydride obtained *via* the liquid ammonia reaction decomposed between $-100°$ and $-78°$, and its decomposition involving a red-solid intermediate was accounted for in terms of the reactions,

$$2(CH_3)_3PbH \xrightarrow{-100°} (CH_3)_3PbPb(CH_3)_2H + CH_4$$

red solid

$$(CH_3)_3PbPb(CH_3)_2H \longrightarrow (CH_3)_4Pb + Pb + CH_4$$

Hydrogen was also produced when the red solid decomposed.

REFERENCES

The literature pertaining to the chemistry of the Group IV elements has been greatly strengthened by the appearance of the following publications during the last four years. The first three serve as a complete source of information on silicon chemistry, and the fourth provides a complete summary of germanium chemistry.

1. Gmelins *Handbuch der Anorganischen Chemie*, Silicium, Teil C, 1958, Verlag Chemie, GMBH, Weinheim.

2. Gmelins *Handbuch der Anorganischen Chemie*, Silicium, Teil B, 1959, Verlag Chemie, GMBH, Weinheim.

3. *Organosilicon Chemistry*, C. Eaborn, Butterworths, London, 1960.

4. Gmelins *Handbuch der Anorganischen Chemie*, Germanium, 1958, Verlag Chemie, GMBH, Weinheim.

1. Allen, H.C., and Plyler, E.K., *J. Amer. Chem. Soc.*, **80,** 2673 (1958).

2. Altshuller, A.P., *J. Chem. Phys.*, **23,** 761 (1955).

3. Amberger, E., *Angew. Chem.*, **71,** 372 (1959).

4. Amberger, E., *Angew. Chem.*, **72,** 78 (1960).

5. Amberger, E., *Angew. Chem.*, **72,** 494 (1960).

6. Amberger, E., and Boeters, H., *Angew. Chem.*, **73,** 114 (1961).

7. Anderson, H.H., *J. Amer. Chem. Soc.*, **78,** 1692 (1956); **79,** 326 (1957).

8. Anderson, H.H., *J. Amer. Chem. Soc.*, **79,** 4913 (1957).

9. Anderson, H.H., *J. Amer. Chem. Soc.*, **80,** 5083 (1958); **81,** 1027 (1959).

10. Anderson, H.H., *J. Amer. Chem. Soc.*, **82,** 3016 (1960); **83,** 547 (1961).

11. Aylett, B.J., *J. Inorg. Nucl. Chem.*, **2,** 325 (1956).

12. Aylett, B.J., Abstracts XVII International Congress of Pure and Applied Chemistry, **1,** 50 (1959).

13. Aylett, B.J., *J. Inorg. Nucl. Chem.*, **15,** 87 (1960).

14. Aylett, B.J., and Ellis, I.A., *J. Chem. Soc.*, 3415 (1960).

15. Aylett, B.J., Emeléus, H.J., and Maddock, A.G., *J. Inorg. Nucl. Chem.*, **1,** 187 (1955).

16. Aylett, B.J., Hall, J.R., McKean, D.C., Taylor, R., and Woodward, L.A., *Spectrochimica Acta*, **16,** 747 (1960).

17. Bak, B., Bruhn, J., and Rastrup-Anderson, J., *J. Chem. Phys.*, **21,** 753 (1953).

18. Bak, B., Bruhn, J , and Rastrup-Anderson, J., *J. Chem. Phys.*, **21,** 752 (1953); *idem. Acta Chem. Scand.*, **8,** 367 (1954).

19. Ball, D.F., Goggin, P.L., McKean, D.C., and Woodward, L.A., *Spectrochimica Acta*, **16,** 1358 (1960).

20. Barry, A.J., British Patent 622,970 (1947/49); *C.A.*, **44,** 658i (1950)

21. Barry, A.J., DePree, L., Gilkey, J.W., and Hook, D.E., *J. Amer. Chem. Soc.*, **69,** 2916 (1947).

22. Barry, A.J., and DePree, L., U.S. Patent 2,488,457 (1949); *C.A.*, **44,** 2547 (1950).

23. Bartell, L.S., and Bonham, R.A., *J. Chem. Phys.*, **31,** 400 (1959).

24. Bassett, E.A., Emblem, H.G., Frankel, M., and Ridge, D., *J. Soc. Chem. Ind.*, **67**, 177 (1948).

25. Batuev, M.I., Ponomarenko, V.A., Matveeva, A.D., and Petrov, A.D., *Doklady Akad. Nauk S.S.S.R.*, **95**, 805 (1954); *C.A.*, **49**, 6089e (1955).

26. Becker, W.E., and Cook, S.E., *J. Amer. Chem. Soc.*, **82**, 6264 (1960).

26a. Benkeser, R.A., Grossman, R.F., and Stanton, G.M., *J. Amer. Chem. Soc.*, **83**, 5029 (1961).

27. Benkeser, R.A., Landesman, H., and Foster, D.J., *J. Amer. Chem. Soc.*, **74**, 648 (1952).

28. Benkeser, R.A., and Riel, F.J., *J. Amer. Chem. Soc.*, **73**, 3472 (1951).

29. Bethke, G.W., and Wilson, M.K., *J. Chem. Phys.*, **26**, 1107 (1957).

30. Bither, T.A., Knoth, W.H., Lindsey, R.V., and Sharkey, W.H., *J. Amer. Chem. Soc.*, **80**, 4151 (1958).

31. Bond, A.C., and Brockway, L.O., *J. Amer. Chem. Soc.*, **76**, 3312 (1954).

32. Booth, H.S., and Jarry, R.L., *J. Amer. Chem. Soc.*, **71**, 971 (1949).

33. Booth, H.S., and Stillwell, W.D., *J. Amer. Chem. Soc.*, **56**, 1529 (1934).

34. Booth, H.S., and Stillwell, W.D., *J. Amer. Chem. Soc.*, **56**, 1531 (1934).

35. Borer, K., and Phillips, C.S.G., *Proc. Chem. Soc.*, 189 (1959).

36. Borisov, S.N., Voronkov, M.G., and Dolgov, B.N., *Doklady Akad. Nauk S.S.S.R.*, **114**, 93 (1957); *C.A.*, **52**, 1057 (1958).

37. Boyd, D.R.J., *J. Chem. Phys.*, **23**, 922 (1955).

38. Brewer, F.M., and Dennis, L.M., *J. Phys. Chem.*, **31**, 1526 (1927).

39. Brimm, E.O., and Humphreys, H.M., *J. Phys. Chem.*, **61**, 829 (1957)

40. Brinckman, F.E., and Stone, F.G.A., *J. Inorg. Nucl. Chem.*, **11**, 24 (1959).

41. Brinckman, F.E., and Stone, F.G.A., *J. Amer. Chem. Soc.*, **82**, 6235 (1960).

42. Brockway, L.O., and Beach, J.Y., *J. Amer. Chem. Soc.*, **60**, 1836 (1938).

43. Brockway, L.O., and Coop, I.E., *Trans. Faraday Soc.*, **34**, 1429 (1938).

44. Brown, H.C., Bartholomay, H., and Taylor, M.D., *J. Amer. Chem. Soc.*, **66**, 435 (1944).

45. Buff, H., and Wöhler, F., *Annalen*, **104**, 94 (1857).

46. Burg, A.B., *J. Amer. Chem. Soc.*, **62,** 2228 (1940).

47. Burg, A.B., and Banus, J., *J. Amer. Chem. Soc.*, **76,** 3903 (1954).

48. Burg, A.B., and Kuljian, E.S., *J. Amer. Chem. Soc.*, **72,** 3103 (1950).

49. Burkhard, C.A., and Krieble, R.H., *J. Amer. Chem. Soc.*, **69,** 2687 (1947).

50. Černý, C., and Erdos, E., *Chem. Listy*, **47,** 1742, 1745 (1953).

51. Chambers, R.F., and Sherer, P.C., *J. Amer. Chem. Soc.*, **48,** 1054 (1926).

52. Chatt, J., and Williams, A.A., *J. Chem. Soc.*, 688 (1956).

53. Clasen, H., *Angew. Chem.*, **70,** 179 (1958).

54. Clusius, K., and Diekel, G., *Z. phys. Chem.*, **51B,** 348 (1942).

55. Cochran, E.L., Fourth International Symposium on Free Radical Stabilization, *Natl. Bureau Standards*, 1959. Quoted in "Formation and Trapping of Free Radicals" (Eds. Bass and Broida), Academic Press, 1960, p. 238.

56. Cottrell, T.L., "The Strengths of Chemical Bonds," Butterworths, London, 1958.

57. Coulson, C.A., "Valence," Oxford University Press, 1961.

58. Cowley, A.W., Fairbrother, F., and Scott, N., *J. Chem. Soc.*, 717 (1959).

59. Curl, R.F., and Pitzer, K.S., *J. Amer. Chem. Soc.*, **80,** 2371 (1958).

60. Curry, J.W., *J. Amer. Chem. Soc.*, **78,** 1686 (1956).

61. Dailey, B.P., Mays, J.M., and Townes, C.H., *Phys. Rev.*, **76,** 136 (1949).

62. Dannels, B.F., and Post, H.W., *J. Org. Chem.*, **22,** 748 (1957).

63. Daudel, R., Brion, H., and Odiot, S., *J. Chem. Phys.*, **23,** 2080 (1955).

64. Deans, D.R., and Eaborn, C., *J. Chem. Soc.*, 3169 (1954).

65. Dennis, L.M., Corey, R.B., and Moore, R.W., *J. Amer. Chem. Soc.*, **46,** 657 (1924).

66. Dennis, L.M., and Judy, P.R., *J. Amer. Chem. Soc.*, **51,** 2321 (1929).

67. Dennis, L.M., Orndorff, W.R., and Tabern, D.L., *J. Phys. Chem.*, **30,** 1049 (1926).

68. Dennis, L.M., and Work, R.W., *J. Amer. Chem. Soc.*, **55,** 4486 (1933).

69. Dewar, M.J.S., and Schmeising, H.N., *Tetrahedron*, **5,** 166 (1959).

70. Dewhurst, H.A., and Cooper, G.D., *J. Amer. Chem. Soc.*, **82**, 4220 (1960).

71. Dickens, P.G., and Linnett, J., *Quart. Revs.*, **11**, 291 (1957).

72. Diehl, J.W., and Gilman, H., *Chem. Ind.*, 1095 (1959). See also *J. Org. Chem.*, **26**, 4817 (1961).

73. Dillard, C.R., McNeill, E.H., Simmons, D.E., and Yeldell, J.B., *J. Amer. Chem. Soc.*, **80**, 3607 (1958).

74. Dixon, R.N., and Sheppard, N., *J. Chem. Phys.*, **23**, 215 (1955); *Trans. Faraday Soc.*, **53**, 282 (1957).

75. Downs, A.J., and Ebsworth, E.A.V., *J. Chem. Soc.*, 3516 (1960).

76. Dows, D.A., and Hexter, R.M., *J. Chem. Phys.*, **24**, 1029, 1117 (1956).

76a. Drake, J.E., and Jolly, W.L., *Proc. Chem. Soc.*, 379 (1961).

77. Duffy, R., and Holliday, A.K., *Proc. Chem. Soc.*, 124 (1959).

78. Eaborn, C., "Organosilicon Compounds," Butterworths, London, 1960.

79. Ebsworth, E.A.V., "Volatile Silicon Compounds," Pergamon, 1962.

80. Ebsworth, E.A.V., and Emeléus, H.J., *J. Chem. Soc.*, 2150 (1958).

81. Ebsworth, E.A.V., Hall, J.R., Mackillop, M.J., McKean, D.C., Sheppard, N., and Woodward, L.A., *Spectrochimica Acta*, **13**, 202 (1958).

81a. Ebsworth, E.A.V., and Mays, M.J., *J. Chem. Soc.*, 4879 (1961).

82. Ebsworth, E.A.V., Onyszchuk, M., and Sheppard, N., *J. Chem. Soc.*, 1453 (1958).

83. Ebsworth, E.A.V., and Sheppard, N., *J. Inorg. Nucl. Chem.*, **9**, 95 (1959).

84. Ebsworth, E.A.V., Taylor, R., and Woodward, L.A., *Trans. Faraday Soc.*, **55**, 211 (1959).

85. Ebsworth, E.A.V., and Turner, J.J., Abstracts Vth European Congress on Molecular Spectroscopy, p. 30 (1961).

86. Emeléus, H.J., and Gardner, E.R., *J. Chem. Soc.*, 1900 (1938).

87. Emeléus, H.J., and Jellinek, H.H.G., *Trans. Faraday Soc.*, **40**, 93 (1944).

88. Emeléus, H.J., and Kettle, S.F.A., *J. Chem. Soc.*, 2444 (1958).

89. Emeléus, H.J., MacDiarmid, A.G., and Maddock, A.G., *J. Inorg. Nucl. Chem.*, **1**, 194 (1955).

90. Emeléus, H.J., and Maddock, A.G., *J. Chem. Soc.*, 293 (1944).

91. Emeléus, H.J., Maddock, A.G., and Reid, C., *J. Chem. Soc.*, 353 (1941).

92. Emeléus, H.J., and Miller, N., *J. Chem. Soc.*, 819 (1939).

93. Emeléus, H.J., and Onyszchuk, M., *J. Chem. Soc.*, 604 (1958).

94. Emeléus, H.J., Onyszchuk, M., and Kuchen, W., *Z. anorg. Chem.*, **283**, 74 (1956).

95. Emeléus, H.J., and Reid, C., *J. Chem. Soc.*, 1021 (1939).

96. Emeléus, H.J., and Robinson, S.R., *J. Chem. Soc.*, 1592 (1947).

97. Emeléus, H.J., and Smythe, L.E., *J. Chem. Soc.*, 609 (1958).

98. Emeléus, H.J., and Stewart, K., *J. Chem. Soc.*, 1182 (1935); *idem., ibid.*, 677 (1936).

99. Emeléus, H.J., and Stewart, K., *Trans. Faraday Soc.*, **32,** 1577 (1936).

100. Emeléus, H.J., and Welch, A.J.E., *J. Chem. Soc.*, 1928 (1939).

101. English, W.D., Taurins, A., and Nicholls, R.V.V., *Canadian J. Chem.*, **30,** 646 (1952).

102. Erickson, C.E., and Wagner, G.H., U.S. Patent 2,627,451 (1953); *C.A.*, **48,** 1420b (1954). U.S. Patent 2,735,861 (1956); *C.A.*, **50,** 13986b (1956).

103. Evers, E.C., Freitag, W.O., Keith, J.N., Kriner, W.A., MacDiarmid, A.G., and Sujishi, S., *J. Amer. Chem. Soc.*, **81,** 4493 (1959).

104. Evers, E.C., Freitag, W.O., Kriner, W.A., MacDiarmid, A.G., and Sujishi, S., *J. Inorg. Nucl. Chem.*, **13,** 239 (1960).

105. Ewing, V.C., and Sutton, L.E., unpublished observations quoted in reference 222.

106. Fehér, F., and Tromm, N., *Z. anorg. Chem.*, **282,** 29 (1955).

107. Fensham, P.J., Tamaru, K., Boudart, M., and Taylor, H., *J. Phys. Chem.*. **59,** 806 (1955).

108. Fergusson, J.E., Grant, D.K., Hickford, R.H., and Wilkins, C.J., *J. Chem. Soc.*, 99 (1959).

109. Finholt, A.E., *Nuclear Sci. Abstr.*, 6, 617 (1952).

110. Finholt, A.E., Bond, A.C., and Schlesinger, H.I., *J. Amer. Chem. Soc.*, **69,** 1199 (1947).

111. Finholt, A.E., Bond, A.C., Wilzbach, K.E., and Schlesinger, H.I., *J Amer. Chem. Soc.*, **69,** 2692 (1947).

112. Fischer, A.K., West, R.C., and Rochow, E.G., *J. Amer. Chem. Soc.*, **76**, 5878 (1954).

113. Fritz, G., *Z. Naturforsch.*, **7b**, 207 (1952).

114. Fritz, G., *Z. anorg. Chem.*, **273**, 275 (1953).

115. Fritz, G., *Z. Naturforsch.*, **8b**, 776 (1953).

116. Fritz, G., *Z. anorg. Chem.*, **280**, 134 (1955).

117. Fritz, G., *Z. Naturforsch.*, **10b**, 423 (1955).

118. Fritz, G., *Angew. Chem.*, **70**, 701 (1958).

119. Fritz, G., and Berkenhoff, H.O., *Z. anorg. Chem.*, **289**, 250 (1957).

120. Fritz, G., and Grobe, J., *Z. anorg. Chem.*, **299**, 302 (1959).

120a. Fritz, G., and Grobe, J., *Z. anorg. Chem.*, **311**, 325 (1961).

121. Fritz, G., and Kautsky, H., British Patent 760,360 (1956); *C.A.*, **51**, 11757h (1957).

122. Fritz, G., and Ksinsik, D., *Z. anorg. Chem.*, **304**, 242 (1960).

123. Fritz, G., and Kummer, D., *Z. anorg. Chem.*, **304**, 322 (1960).

124. Fritz, G., and Kummer, D., *Z. anorg. Chem.*, **306**, 191 (1960).

125. Fritz, G., and Kummer, D., *Chem. Ber.*, **94**, 1143 (1961).

125a. Fritz, G., and Kummer, D., *Z. anorg. Chem.*, **308**, 105 (1961).

125b. Fritz, G., and Kummer, D., *Z. anorg. Chem.*, **310**, 327 (1961).

126. Fritz, G., and Raabe, B., *Z. anorg. Chem.*, **299**, 232 (1959).

127. Fritz, G., and Teichmann, G., *Angew. Chem.*, **70**, 701 (1958).

128. Fritz, G., and Thielking, H., *Z. anorg. Chem.*, **306**, 40 (1960); and references cited therein.

129. Frost, R.E., and Rochow, E.G., *J. Inorg. Nucl. Chem.*, **5**, 207 (1958).

130. Fuchs, R., and Gilman, H., *J. Org. Chem.*, **22**, 1009 (1957).

131. Gattermann, L., *Ber.*, **22**, 186 (1899).

132. Gauthier, *Ann. chim. Phys.*, **17**, 203 (1869).

133. George, P.D., Prober, M., and Elliott, J.R., *Chemical Reviews*, **56**, 1065 (1956); and references cited therein.

134. Geyer, A.M., and Haszeldine, R.N., *J. Chem. Soc.*, 1038 (1957).

135. Gilman, H., Brooks, H.G., and Hughes, M.B., *J. Org. Chem.*, **23**, 1398 (1958).

136. Gilman, H., and Dunn, G.E., *Chemical Reviews*, **52**, 77 (1953); and references cited therein.

137. Gilman, H., and Eisch, J., *J. Org. Chem.*, **20**, 763 (1955).

138. Gilman, H., and Gerow, C.W., *J. Amer. Chem. Soc.*, **78**, 5435 (1956).

139. Gilman, H., and Gerow, C.W., *J. Amer. Chem. Soc.*, **79**, 342 (1957).

140. Gilman, H., and Marrs, O.L., *J. Org. Chem.*, **25**, 1194 (1960).

141. Gilman, H., and Meals, R.N., *J. Org. Chem.*, **23**, 326 (1958).

142. Gilman, H., and Melvin, H.W., *J. Amer. Chem. Soc.*, **71**, 4050 (1949).

143. Gilman, H., and Rosenberg, S.D., *J. Amer. Chem. Soc.*, **75**, 3592 (1953).

144. Gilman, H., and Zuech, E.A., *J. Amer. Chem. Soc.*, **81**, 5925 (1959).

145. Glarum, S.N., and Kraus, C.A., *J. Amer. Chem. Soc.*, **72**, 5398 (1950).

146. Glemser, O., and Lohmann, W., *Z. anorg. Chem.*, **275**, 260 (1954).

147. Graham, W.A.G., and Stone, F.G.A., *J. Inorg. Nucl. Chem.*, **3**, 164 (1956).

147a. Griffiths, J.E. and McAfee, K.B., *Proc. Chem. Soc.*, 456 (1961).

148. Griffiths, S.T., and Wilson, R.R., *Combustion and Flame*, **2**, 244 (1958).

149. Gunn, S.R., and Green, L.G., *J. Phys. Chem.*, **65**, 779 (1961).

150. Gutowsky, H.S., and Stejskal, E.O., *J. Chem. Phys.*, **22**, 939 (1954).

151. Hawkins, J.A., Polo, S.R., and Wilson, M.K., *J. Chem. Phys.*, **21**, 1122 (1953).

152. Hawkins, J.A., and Wilson, M.K., *J. Chem. Phys.*, **21**, 360 (1953).

153. Heath, G.A., Thomas, L.F., and Sheridan, J., *Trans. Faraday Soc.*, **50**, 779 (1954).

154. Hedberg, K., *J. Amer. Chem. Soc.*, **77**, 6491 (1955).

155. Hemptinne, M., and Wouters, J., *Nature*, **138**, 884 (1936).

155a. Henry, M.C., and Downey, M.F., *J. Org. Chem.*, **26**, 2299 (1961).

156. Henry, M.C., and Noltes, J.G., *J. Amer. Chem. Soc.*, **82**, 558 (1960).

157. Henry, M.C., and Noltes, J.G., *J. Amer. Chem. Soc.*, **82,** 561 (1960).

158. Hogness, T.R., and Johnson, W.C., *J. Amer. Chem. Soc.*, **54,** 3583 (1932).

159. Hogness, T.R., Wilson, T.L., and Johnson, W.C., *J. Amer. Chem. Soc.*, **58,** 108 (1936).

160. Hurd, D.T., *J. Amer. Chem. Soc.*, **69,** 1647 (1947).

161. Jenkins, D.R., Kewley, R., and Sugden, T.M., *Proc. Chem. Soc.*, 220 (1960).

162. Jenkins, J.W., Lavery, N.L., Guenther, P.R., and Post, H.W., *J. Org. Chem.*, **13,** 862 (1948).

163. Jenkins, J.W., and Post, H.W., *J. Org. Chem.*, **15,** 552 (1950).

164. Jenkins, J.W., and Post, H.W., *J. Org. Chem.*, **15,** 556 (1950).

165. Johnson, O.H., *Chemical Reviews*, **48,** 259 (1951).

166. Johnson, O.H., and Harris, D.M., *J. Amer. Chem. Soc.*, **72,** 5564 (1950).

167. Johnson, O.H., and Harris, D.M., *J. Amer. Chem. Soc.*, **72,** 5566 (1950).

168. Johnson, O.H., and Jones, L.V., *J. Org. Chem.*, **17,** 1172 (1952).

169. Johnson, W.C., and Hogness, T.R., *J. Amer. Chem. Soc.*, **56,** 1252 (1934).

170. Johnson, W.C., and Isenberg, S., *J. Amer. Chem. Soc.*, **57,** 1349 (1935).

171. Jolly, W.L., *Angew. Chem.*, **72,** 268 (1960).

172. Jolly, W.L., *J. Amer. Chem. Soc.*, **83,** 335 (1961).

173. Kaesz, H.D., and Stone, F.G.A., *J. Chem. Soc.*, 1433 (1957).

174. Kaplan, L., and Wilzbach, K.E., *J. Amer. Chem. Soc.*, **77,** 1297 (1955); and references cited therein.

175. Kautsky, H., and Richter, T., *Z. Naturforsch.*, **11b,** 365 (1956).

176. Kautsky, H., and Siebel, H.P., *Z. anorg. Chem.*, **273,** 113 (1953).

177. Kaye, S., and Tannenbaum, S., *J. Org. Chem.*, **18,** 1750 (1953).

178. Keidel, F.A., quoted by S.H. Bauer and P. Anderson, *Ann. Rev. Phys. Chem.*, **4,** 236 (1953).

179. Kettle, S.F.A., *J. Chem. Soc.*, 2936 (1959).

179a. Kettle, S.F.A., *J. Chem. Soc.*, 2569 (1961).

180. Kewley, R., Murt, U.S.R., and Sugden, T.M., unpublished results quoted in reference 79.

181. Kilb, R.W., and Pierce, L., *J. Chem. Phys.*, **27**, 108 (1957).

182. Kniseley, R.N., Fassel, V.A., and Conrad, E.E., *Spectrochimica Acta*, **15**, 651 (1959).

183. Kraus, C.A., and Carney, E.S., *J. Amer. Chem. Soc.*, **56**, 765 (1934).

184. Kraus, C.A., and Flood, E.A., *J. Amer. Chem. Soc.*, **54**, 1635 (1932).

185. Kraus, C.A., and Foster, L.S., *J. Amer. Chem. Soc.*, **49**, 457 (1927).

186. Kraus, C.A., and Greer, W.N., *J. Amer. Chem. Soc.*, **44**, 2629 (1922).

187. Kraus, C.A., and Nelson, W.K., *J. Amer. Chem. Soc.*, **56**, 195 (1934).

188. Krespan, C.G., and Engelhardt, V.A., *J. Org. Chem.*, **23**, 1565 (1958).

189. Kriner, W.A., MacDiarmid, A.G., and Evers, E.C., *J. Amer. Chem. Soc.*, **80**, 1546 (1958).

190. Krisher, L.C., and Pierce, L., *J. Chem. Phys.*, **32**, 1619 (1960).

191. Kuchen. W., *Z. anorg. Chem.*, **288**, 101 (1956).

192. Kuivila, H.G., and Beumal, O.F., *J. Amer. Chem. Soc.*, **80**, 3798 (1958); **83**, 1246 (1961).

192a. Kuivila, H.G., Sawyer, A.K., and Armour, A.G., *J. Org. Chem.*, **26**, 1426 (1961).

193. Kumada, M., *J. Inst. Polytech. Osaka City Univ.*, **2**, 131 (1952); *C.A.*, **48**, 11303d (1954).

194. Kumada, M., and Tarama, K., *J. Chem. Soc. Japan, Ind. Chem. Sect.*, **54**, 769 (1951); *C.A.*, **48**, 3889b (1954).

195. Langmuir, I., *J. Amer. Chem. Soc.*, **41**, 868, 1543 (1919).

196. Laurie, V.W., *J. Chem. Phys.*, **26**, 1359 (1957).

196a. Laurie, V.W., *J. Chem. Phys.*, **30**, 1210 (1959).

197. Lesbre, M., and Buisson, R., *Bull. Soc. chim. France.* 1204 (1957).

198. Lewis, G.N., *J. Amer. Chem. Soc.*, **38**, 762 (1916).

199. Lewis, R.N., *J. Amer. Chem. Soc.*, **69**, 717 (1947).

200. Lide, D.R., *J. Chem. Phys.*, **19**, 1605 (1951).

201. Lindeman, L.P., and Wilson, M.K., *J. Chem. Phys.*, **22**, 1723 (1954).

202. Lindeman, L.P., and Wilson, M.K., *Z. phys. Chem.*, **9**, 29 (1956).

203. Lindeman, L.P., and Wilson, M.K., *Spectrochimica Acta*, **9**, 47 (1957).

204. Linton, H.R., and Nixon, E.R., *J. Chem. Phys.*, **28**, 990 (1958).

205. Linton, H.R., and Nixon, E.R., *J. Chem. Phys.*, **29**, 921 (1958).

206. Linton, H.R., and Nixon, E.R., *Spectrochimica Acta*, **10**, 299 (1958).

207. Linton, H.R., and Nixon, E.R., *Spectrochimica Acta*, **12**, 41 (1958).

208. Linton, H.R., and Nixon, E.R., *Spectrochimica Acta*, **15**, 146 (1959).

209. Lord, R.C., Mayo, D.W., Opitz, H.E., and Peake, J.S., *Spectrochimica Acta*, **12**, 147 (1958).

210. Lord, R.C., Robinson, D.W., and Schumb, W.C., *J. Amer. Chem. Soc.*, **78**, 1327 (1956).

211. Lord, R.C., and Steese, C.M., *J. Chem. Phys.*, **22**, 542 (1954).

212. MacDiarmid, A.G., *Quart. Revs.*, **10**, 208 (1956).

213. MacDiarmid, A.G., *J. Inorg. Nucl. Chem.*, **2**, 88 (1956).

214. MacDiarmid, A.G., *Advances in Inorganic Chemistry and Radiochemistry* (Eds. H.J. Emeléus and A.G. Sharpe), **3**, 207 (1961), Academic Press, N.Y.

215. MacDiarmid, A.G., and Maddock, A.G., *J. Inorg. Nucl. Chem.*, **1**, 411 (1955).

216. Macklen, E.D., *J. Chem. Soc.*, 1984 (1959).

217. Macklen, E.D., *J. Chem. Soc.*, 1989 (1959).

218. May, L., and Dillard, C.R., *J. Chem. Phys.*, **34**, 694 (1961).

219. Mayo, D.W., Opitz, H.E., and Peake, J.S., *J. Chem. Phys.*, **23**, 1344 (1955).

220. Mays, J.M., and Dailey, B.P., *J. Chem. Phys.*, **20**, 1695 (1952).

220a. Mazeroless, P., and Lesbre, M., *Compt. rend.*, **248**, 2018 (1959).

221. McKean, D.C., *Spectrochimica Acta*, **13**, 38 (1958).

222. McKean, D.C., *Proc. Chem. Soc.*, 321 (1959).

223. McKenzie, C.A., Mills, A.P., and Scott, J.M., *J. Amer. Chem. Soc.*, **72**, 2032 (1950).

224. McCusker, P.A., and Reilly, E.L., *J. Amer. Chem. Soc.*, **75**, 1583 (1953).

225. Meal, J.H., and Wilson, M.K., *J. Chem. Phys.*, **24**, 385 (1956).

226. Meals, R.N., *J. Amer. Chem. Soc.*, **68**, 1880 (1946).

227. Miller, W.S., Peake, J.S., and Nebergall, W.H., *J. Amer. Chem. Soc.*, **79**, 5604 (1957).

228. Moissan, H., and Holt, *Compt. rend.*, **135**, 78 (1902).

229. Moulton, C.W., and Miller, J.G., *J. Amer. Chem. Soc.*, **78**, 2702 (1956).

229a. Muller, N., and Bracken, R.C., *J. Chem. Phys.*, **32**, 1577 (1960).

230. Mulliken, R.S., *J. Amer. Chem. Soc.*, **72**, 4493 (1950).

231. Mulliken, R.S., *Tetrahedron*, **5**, 253 (1959).

232. Nebergall, W.H., *J. Amer. Chem. Soc.*, **72**, 4702 (1950).

233. Nebergall, W.H., Peake, J.S., and Opitz, H.E., *Naturwiss.*, 179 (1960).

234. Newman, C., O'Loane, J.K., Polo, S.R., and Wilson, M.K., *J. Chem. Phys.*, **25**, 855 (1956).

235. Newman, C., Polo, S.R., and Wilson, M.K., *Spectrochimica Acta*, **15**, 793 (1959).

236. Noltes, J.G., Doctoral Thesis, University of Utrecht, 1958.

237. Onyszchuk, M., *Canadian J. Chem.*, **39**, 808 (1961).

238. Opitz, H.E., Peake, J.S., and Nebergall, W.H., *J. Amer. Chem. Soc.*, **78**, 292 (1956).

239. O'Reilly, J.M., and Pierce, L., *J. Chem. Phys.*, **34**, 1176 (1961).

240. Paneth, F., *Z. Elektrochem.*, **26**, 452 (1920); **29**, 97 (1923).

241. Paneth, F., and Fürth, K., *Ber.*, **52**, 2020 (1919).

242. Paneth, F., Matthies, M., and Schmidt-Hebbel, E., *Ber.*, **55**, 775, 2615 (1922).

243. Paneth, F., and Nörring, O., *Ber.*, **53**, 1693 (1920).

244. Pape, C., *Annalen*, **222**, 354 (1884).

245. Pauling, L., Kekule Symposium on Theoretical Organic Chemistry, Chemical Society London, 1958, Butterworths (1959).

246. Pauling, L., Laubengayer, A.W., and Hoard, J.L., *J. Amer. Chem. Soc.* **60**, 1605 (1938).

247. Peake, J.S., Nebergall, W.H., and Yun Ti Chen, *J. Amer. Chem. Soc.*, **74,** 1526 (1952).

248. Petrov, A.D., and Ponomarenko, V.A., *Doklady Akad. Nauk S.S.S.R.*, **90,** 387 (1953); *C.A.*, **48,** 5080c (1954).

249. Pierce, L., *J. Chem. Phys.*, **29,** 383 (1958).

250. Pierce, L., *J. Chem. Phys.*, **34,** 498 (1961).

251. Pierce, L., and Petersen, D.H., *J. Chem. Phys.*, **33,** 907 (1960).

252. Piper, T.S., and Wilson, M.K., *J. Inorg. Nucl. Chem.*, **4,** 22 (1957).

253. Pitzer, K.S., *J. Amer. Chem. Soc.*, **70,** 2140 (1948).

254. Polo, S.R., and Wilson, M.K., *J. Chem. Phys.*, **22,** 1559 (1954).

255. Ponomarenko, V.A., and Miranov, V.F., *Bull. Acad. Sci. U.S.S.R.*, 423 (1954); *C.A.*, **49,** 9495e (1955).

256. Price, F.P., *J. Amer. Chem. Soc.*, **69,** 2600 (1947).

257. Riemschneider, R., Menge, K., and Klang, P., *Z. Naturforsch.*, **11b,** 115 (1956).

258. Ring, M.A., and Ritter, D.M., *J. Amer. Chem. Soc.*, **83,** 802 (1961).

259. Rosenberg, S.D., Walburn, J.J., Stankovich, T.D., Balint, A.E., and Ramsden, H.E., *J. Org. Chem.*, **22,** 1200 (1957).

260. Royen, P., and Schwarz, R., *Z. anorg. Chem.*, **211,** 412 (1933); **215,** 288, 295 (1933).

261. Ruff, O., *Ber.*, **41,** 3738 (1908).

262. Saalfeld, F.E., and Sves, H.J., *J. Inorg. Nucl. Chem.*, **18,** 98 (1961).

263. Sauer, R.O., Scheiber, W.J., and Brewer, S.D., *J. Amer. Chem. Soc.*, **68,** 962 (1946).

263a. Sawyer, A.K., and Kuivila, H.G., *Chem. Ind.*, 260 (1961).

264. Schaeffer, G.W., and Emilius, M., *J. Amer. Chem. Soc.*, **76,** 1203 (1954).

265. Schaeffer, R., and Ross, L., *J. Amer. Chem. Soc.*, **81,** 3486 (1959).

265a. Schaeffer, R., and Wells, R., unpublished observations. See "Studies of Light Weight Elements" by R. Schaeffer *et al*; Technical Report No. 2, Contract Nonr-908 (14) August, 1961.

266. Schäfer, K., and Gonzalez-Barredo, J.M., *Z. physik. Chem.*, **193,** 334 (1944).

267. Schalla, R.L., McDonald, G.E., and Gerstein, M., Fifth Symposium on Combustion, pages 705-710, Reinhold, N.Y., 1955.

268. Schenck, R., *Rec. Trav. chim.*, **41**, 569 (1922).

269. Schmeisser, M., and Müller, H., *Angew. Chem.*, **69**, 781 (1957).

270. Schomaker, V., and Stevenson, D.P., *J. Amer. Chem. Soc.*, **63**, 37 (1941).

271. Schott, G., Herrmann, W., and Hirschmann, E., *Angew. Chem.*, **68**, 213 (1956).

272. Schumb, W.C., "Inorganic Syntheses" (Ed. H.S. Booth), Vol. I., McGraw-Hill, New York, 1939.

273. Schumb, W.C., and Robinson, D.W., *J. Amer. Chem. Soc.*, **77**, 5294 (1955).

274. Schumb, W.C., and Young, R.C., *J. Amer. Chem. Soc.*, **52**, 1464 (1930).

275. Sharbaugh, A.H., Bragg, J.K., Madison, T.C., and Thomas, V.G., *Phys. Revs.*, **76**, 1419 (1949).

276. Sheehan, W.F., and Schomaker, V., *J. Amer. Chem. Soc.*, **74**, 3956 (1952).

277. Sheridan, J., and Gordy, W., *J. Chem. Phys.*, **19**, 965 (1951).

278. Sheridan, J., and Turner, A.C., *Proc. Chem. Soc.*, 21 (1960).

279. Skinner, M.A., *Trans. Faraday Soc.*, **41**, 645 (1945).

280. Smith, A.L., *Spectrochimica Acta*, **16**, 87 (1960).

281. Smith, A.L., and Angelotti, N.C., *Spectrochimica Acta*, **15**, 412 (1959).

282. Smolin, E., *Tetrahedron Letters*, 143 (1961).

283. Sommer, L.H., Abstracts XVII International Congress of Pure and Applied Chemistry, **1**, 52 (1959).

284. Sommer, L.H., Pietrusza, E.W., and Whitmore, F.C., *J. Amer. Chem. Soc.*, **69**, 188 (1947); **70**, 484 (1948).

285. Speier, J.L., and Zimmerman, R., *J. Amer. Chem. Soc.*, **77**, 6395 (1955).

286. Speier, J.L., Zimmerman, R., and Webster, J., *J. Amer. Chem. Soc.*, **78**, 2278 (1956).

287. Spitzer, R., Howell, W.J., and Schomaker, V., *J. Amer. Chem. Soc.*, **64**, 62 (1942).

288. Srivastava, T.N., and Onyszchuk, M., Abstracts 137th Meeting Am. Chem. Soc., Cleveland, Ohio, 1960. p. 36M.

289. Srivastave, T.N., and Onyszchuk, M., *Proc. Chem. Soc.*, 205 (1961).

290. Sternbach, B., and MacDiarmid, A.G., *J. Amer. Chem. Soc.*, **81,** 5109 (1959).

290a. Sternbach, B., and MacDiarmid, A.G., *J. Amer. Chem. Soc.*, **83,** 3384 (1961).

291. Steward, W.B., and Nielsen, H.H., *Phys. Rev.*, **47,** 828 (1935).

292. Stitt, F., and Yost, D.M., *J. Chem. Phys.*, **5,** 90 (1937).

293. Stock, A., "Hydrides of Boron and Silicon," Cornell University Press, 1933.

294. Stock, A., and Somieski, C., *Ber.*, **52,** 695 (1919); see also reference 293.

295. Stokland, K., *Trans. Faraday Soc.*, **44,** 545 (1948).

296. Stone, F.G.A., *Quart. Revs.*, **9,** 174 (1955); and references cited therein.

297. Stone, F.G.A., *Chemical Reviews*, **58,** 101 (1958).

298. Stone, F.G.A., *Advances in Inorganic Chemistry and Radiochemistry* (Eds. H.J. Emeléus and A.G. Sharpe), **2,** 279 (1960), Academic Press, N.Y.

299. Stone, F.G.A., *Endeavour*, **78,** 61 (1961).

300. Stone, F.G.A., and Seyferth, D., *J. Inorg. Nucl. Chem.*, **1,** 112 (1955).

301. Straley, J.W., Tindal, C.H., and Nielsen, H.H., *Phys. Rev.*, **62,** 161 (1942).

302. Strother, C.O., and Wagner, G.H., U.S. Patent 2,532,430 (1947/50); *C.A.*, **45,** 2968f (1951).

303. Sujishi, S., Abstracts XVII International Congress of Pure and Applied Chem., **1,** 53 (1959).

304. Sujishi, S., and Keith, J.N., *J. Amer. Chem. Soc.*, **80,** 4138 (1958).

305. Sujishi, S., and Manasevit, H.M., Abstracts of 135th Meeting Amer. Chem. Soc., Boston, Mass., p. 48M, 1959.

306. Sujishi, S., and Witz, S., *J. Amer. Chem. Soc.*, **76,** 4631 (1954).

307. Sujishi, S., and Witz, S., *J. Amer. Chem. Soc.*, **79,** 2447 (1957).

308. Swalen, J.D., and Stoicheff, B.P., *J. Chem. Phys.*, **28,** 671 (1958).

309. Tamaru, K., *J. Phys. Chem.*, **60,** 610 (1956).

310. Tamaru, K., Boudart, M., and Taylor, H., *J. Phys. Chem.*, **59,** 801 (1955).

311. Tannenbaum, S., *J. Amer. Chem. Soc.*, **76,** 1027 (1954).

312. Tannenbaum, S., Kaye, S., and Lewenz, G.F., *J. Amer. Chem. Soc.*, **75,** 3753 (1953).

313. Teal, G.K., and Kraus, C.A., *J. Amer. Chem. Soc.*, **72,** 4706 (1950).

314. Thomas, A.B., and Rochow, E.G., *J. Amer. Chem. Soc.*, **79,** 1843 (1957).

315. Thompson, H.W., *Spectrochimica Acta*, **16,** 238 (1960).

316. Tindal, C.H., Straley, J.W., and Nielsen, H.H., *Phys. Rev.*, **62**,151 (1942).

317. Topchiev, A.V., Nametkin, N.S., and Chernysheva, T.I., *Doklady Akad. Nauk S.S.S.R.*, **118,** 517 (1958); *C.A.*, **52,** 10922 (1958).

318. van Artsdalen, E.R., and Gavis, J., *J. Amer. Chem. Soc.*, **74,** 3196 (1952).

319. van der Kelen, G.P., and van de Vandel, D.F., *Bull. Soc. chim. Belg.*, **69,** 504 (1960).

320. van der Kerk, G.J.M., Noltes, J.G., and Luitjen, J.G.A., *J. Appl. Chem.*, **7,** 356 (1957); *Chem. Ind.*, 352 (1956).

321. van der Kerk, G.J.M., Noltes, J.G., and Luitjen, J.G.A., *J. Appl. Chem.*, **7,** 366 (1957).

322. van der Kerk, G.J.M., Noltes, J.G., and Luitjen, J.G.A., *Chem. Ind.*, 1290 (1958).

323. van der Kerk, G.J.M., and Noltes, J.G., *J. Appl. Chem.*, **9,** 106 (1959).

324. Venkateswarlu, P., Mockler, R.C., and Gordy, W., *J. Chem. Phys.*, **21,** 1713 (1953).

325. Voegelen, E., *Z. anorg. Chem.*, **30,** 325 (1902).

326. Voronkov, M.G., and Khudobin, Y.I., *Izvest. Akad. Nauk S.S.S.R., Otdel. khim. Nauk*, 805 (1956); *C.A.*, **51,** 3440f (1957).

327. Ward, L.G.L., and MacDiarmid, A.G., *J. Amer. Chem. Soc.*, **82,** 2151 (1960).

328. Ward, L.G.L., and MacDiarmid, A.G., Abstracts 137th Meeting Amer. Chem. Soc., Cleveland, Ohio, p. 11M, 1960.

328a. Ward, L.G.L., and MacDiarmid, A.G., *J. Inorg. Nucl. Chem.*, **20,** 345 (1961).

329. Warren, H.N., *Chem. News*, **60,** 158 (1889).

330. Webster, D.E., *J. Chem. Soc.*, 5132 (1960).

331. Wells, A.F., *J. Chem. Soc.*, 55 (1949).

332. West, R., *J. Amer. Chem. Soc.*, **75,** 6080 (1953).

333. West, R., and Rochow, E.G., *J. Org. Chem.*, **18,** 303 (1953).

334. Westermark, H., *Acta. Chem. Scand.*, **8,** 1830 (1954).

335. White, D.G., and Rochow, E.G., *J. Amer. Chem. Soc.*, **76,** 3897 (1954).

336. Whitmore, F.C., Pietrusza, E.W., and Sommer, L.H., *J. Amer. Chem. Soc.*, **69,** 2108 (1947).

337. Wiberg, E., and Bauer, R., *Z. Naturforsch.*, **6b,** 392 (1951).

338. Wiberg, E., and Simmler, W., *Z. anorg. Chem.*, **283,** 401 (1956).

339. Wilkinson, G.R., and Wilson, M.K., *J. Chem. Phys.*, **25,** 784 (1956).

340. Wilson, E.B., *Advances in Chemical Physics* (Ed. I. Prigogine), **2,** 367 (1959), Interscience, N.Y.

341. Winkler, C., *J. prakt. Chem.*, **142** (N.S. 34), 177 (1886).

342. Winkler, C., *J. prakt. Chem.*, **144** (N.S. 36), 177 (1887).

343. Wittenberg, D., McNinch, H.A., and Gilman, H., *J. Amer. Chem. Soc.*, **80,** 5418 (1958).

344. Wöhler, F., and Buff, H., *Annalen*, **103,** 218 (1857).

345. Wolfe, J.K., and Cook, N.C., U.S. Patent 2,786,862 (1957); *C.A.*, **51,** 13904e (1957).

346. Wouters, J., Hemptinne, M., and Capron, P., *Ann. Soc. sci. Brux.*, Ser. I, **57,** 25 (1937).